CODD'S LAST CASE
and Other Misleading Cases

CODD'S LAST CASE
AND
OTHER
MISLEADING CASES

Reported and edited

by

A. P. HERBERT

METHUEN & CO. LTD. LONDON
36 Essex Street, Strand, W.C.2

First published in 1952

CATALOGUE NO. 5393/U

PRINTED IN GREAT BRITAIN

All these cases, but one, were originally reported in the pages of *Punch*. My thanks to the proprietors for their courteous permission to publish them again. I also thank the Controller of Her Majesty's Stationery Office for permission to include some quotations from *Hansard*.

A. P. H.

TABLE OF CASES

(1) HOGBY, E. A. *v.* HOGBY, W. M.

THE PRICE OF JUSTICE
(Before Mr. Justice Plush)

HIS LORDSHIP to-day delivered an important judgment on the meaning of Magna Carta. He said:

There is not much left of the Great Charter to-day, and what remains is little known to most of the King's subjects, who in these days appear to be more interested in the liberties of Letts, Sudeten Germans, and Czecho-Slovakians than in their own. But members of the legal profession at least still dwell with reverence and contentment on Chapter 29 of the Magna Carta. Many a tired judge or gentleman of the long robe falls decorously to sleep at last with this much-loved enactment under his pillow and in his mind the unforgettable promise of 700 years ago:

> *To no man will we sell, to no man deny, to no man delay, justice or right.*

'To no man will we sell justice. . . .' It is not to be supposed that the enlightened monarch who set his hand to these words had in his mind to diminish or destroy the meagre remuneration of the legal profession. Barristers and solicitors—and even, I suppose, judges—are as well entitled as others to keep body and soul alive by selling their services and their learning to the people. Moreover, like the medical profession, they give much free advice and service to the poor without much gratitude or even acknowledgment from the public.[1]

No, the meaning of the Monarch, I think, is plain. King John undertook, for his heirs and assigns, that the *Crown*

[1] His Majesty's Judges, though their salaries have not been raised since 1832 (when they were free of income-tax), are constantly called upon for heavy extra work on Committees, Commissions of Inquiry, etc.

would not sell justice—that is, that neither the possession of wealth nor the readiness to bribe should be a necessary passport into the Royal Courts of Justice.

This case, not for the first time, reveals how very far we have fallen to-day below the lofty ideals and undertakings of King John. Mr. Hogby has been successful in a law-suit, but he has been required to pay the costs of the unsuccessful party. This at first sight shocking statement is easily explained. The suit was a divorce suit; he is a husband; the other party was his wife; and by a bizarre tradition in this department of justice a husband, innocent or guilty, victorious or not, must always pay the costs of his wife, though the action be erroneously originated by her. This is called the Equality of the Sexes.

To that queer point I shall reluctantly return.

Now, of the costs in question here, some represented the modest fees of barristers and solicitors, some the expenses of witnesses (on both sides), and some the necessary out-of-pocket charges incurred by solicitors in the ordinary conduct of a case. To none of these could Mr. Hogby make reasonable objection, except that under a system of genuine justice they would be paid by his wife, who brought against him a charge of cruelty and was unable to sustain it to the satisfaction of the Court.

But there was also a minor, though, to Mr. Hogby, at least, a substantial charge for what are called court fees. These are the very numerous fixed fees charged by the Crown at various stages of a suit at law. For example, on the filing of each affidavit there is a charge of 2s. 6d., and upon each swearing another half-crown. Here in the bill before me is 'Alimony; application for appointment, each hour or part thereof, 10 shillings. Questions for jury, 10 shillings; settling question for jury, 10 shillings; re-settling questions for jury, 10 shillings. Appeal to Court of Appeal, filing notice and entering, £7; notice of entering, £3'; and so on. At every preliminary stage of the dispute money passes to the Crown; and when at last the litigant is admitted to the Temple of Justice, he is charged by the hour for the time that he spends there. 'Hearing, or trial, of cause—first five hours £2' (or 8s. an hour) 'and for each additional complete hour, 10 shillings.'

It was well said in the House of Commons recently by Mr. Haddock (Ind. Nat.) that, if the Crown must charge for justice, at least the fee should be like the fee for postage: that is to say, it should be the same, however long the journey may be. For it is no fault of one litigant that his plea to the King's judges raises questions more difficult to determine than another's, and will require a longer hearing in court. He is asking for justice, not renting house-property.

Well, if all this is not selling justice, I do not know what is. In the ordinary course, it is true, the party who loses will have to meet these charges, upon the theory that he deserves to pay for taking the time of the Court with a plea now proved to be wrong. But can even this be defended as equitable? He was not to know that he was wrong; and even now it is not certain that he was wrong. For the Court of Appeal might say that he was right. Only the House of Lords can say with certitude and finality that he is wrong; and few of the King's subjects can afford to ask them. Right or wrong, he is entitled to ask for justice (unless he is a frivolous or vexatious litigant, when there are effective ways of dealing with him): and the Crown ought not to make it more difficult for him to obtain justice by charging fees for it. I am told that the Crown makes a profit out of the Courts.

The Attorney-General (Sir Anthony Slatt): Milord, with great respect, I am not sure that that is strictly accurate.

The Judge: It's a very near thing, is it not?

The Attorney-General: If the fees for non-contentious probate business be included, I believe that may be so, milord: but no profit is made from litigation. As to that, milord, may I suggest one possible line of thought? The Crown, in this connection, means the whole body of taxpayers. Would it be fair and equitable if the general taxpayer had to provide all the facilities of the Courts for the benefit of the litigant?

The Judge: Why not? Everybody pays for the police, but

some people use them more than others. Nobody complains. You don't have to pay a special fee every time you have a burglary, or ask a policeman the way. I don't follow you, Sir Anthony.

I will go further. I hold that the Crown not merely ought not, but is unable, to act in this way, by reason of the passage in the Great Charter which I have quoted. The Rules of Court, then, which purport to impose these charges are *ultra vires*, unconstitutional, and of no effect: and Mr. Hogby may continue to decline to pay them.

That, however, does not dispose of his difficulties. There remain the other costs which I have mentioned. These amount to a much larger sum; and they are much larger than they should be in a country which prides itself on its administration of justice. This, again, is the fault not of Parliament but of the Crown.

Mr. Hogby resides in a town in Yorkshire. This is an Assize town—that is to say, it is visited from time to time by two of His Majesty's Judges for the purpose of delivering justice there. If Mr. Hogby had been sued for fraud, for libel, for embezzlement, or for breach of promise, the case could have been heard there, near his own home. But it was a suit for divorce. Now the only divorce cases that can be heard at some Assize Courts (not all of them) are (*a*) undefended cases and (*b*) Poor Persons' cases, defended or not. Mr. Hogby, though poor (he is a school-teacher), is not poor enough to qualify for free legal assistance as a Poor Person. Therefore, if he defends the case, he must travel to the High Court in London, and suffer all the additional expense that that involves.[1]

He must pay not only his own solicitor in Yorkshire but in addition an agent in London—not to mention his wife's solicitor and agent. He must pay for the transport to London, and their accommodation there, not only of his own witnesses but his wife's. He must leave his home, and occupation, for two or three days, for there will be no certainty that his case

[1] Not now.

will be called immediately after his arrival. While they are waiting, though he and his witnesses may be content with a modest hotel and reasonable cuisine, his wife, who knows that she has not to pay, and *ex hypothesi* is not at present well-disposed towards him, has no reason to stint her comfort or that of her witnesses.

Mr. Hogby, he tells us, had saved little, and he was appalled by the prospect of such expenditure. One way out was to allow his wife's case to succeed by default. It would then be heard in his own town as an undefended suit at comparatively small expense. He would be divorced, but not bankrupt. Many men, it is believed, confronted with the same dilemma, have taken that course.

But Mr. Hogby is a school-teacher. If he were to make no answer to a charge of marital cruelty, and for that suffer divorce, he would, he was persuaded, no longer be permitted by the Education Authority to have the care and teaching of children.

It is interesting, by the way, and will be gratifying to many that there is still one profession where divorce is regarded as a handicap. Isn't it, Sir Anthony? Are you awake?

The Attorney-General (Sir Anthony Slatt, K.C.): Yes, milord.

The Judge: Accordingly he fought the case, and, necessarily, in London. He won. The charges against him were struck out. He is not divorced; but he is, to all intents and purposes, bankrupt.

I am now asked to issue a judgment summons against him for the outstanding costs of this unfortunate affair; and, if he does not pay, I suppose that he will go to prison. Two questions will leap at once to the mind of the humane observer: (1) for what good reason am I requested to condemn and punish the husband who was successful in his appeal for justice instead of the wife, who was not? and (2) for what reason could not this comparatively simple case have been heard by one of the King's Judges in Yorkshire, where the costs and inconveniences of Mr. Hogby would have been considerably less?

It is not for me to furnish reasonable answers, if such can be found. It is vain, if it were seemly, to blame Parliament in this affair, for Parliament, I believe, in both cases, has already entrusted the necessary powers to the proper authorities. The remedy, if any, is in the hands of the administration—in other words, of the Crown. All kinds of profound and mystical arguments are used, I know, for the retention of the present system. Since I am dealing with the Crown, which in this case means the learned and illustrious heads of the profession which I adorn, I must not, and shall not, attempt to meet those arguments, though one or two comments may quietly possess my mind.

But here is Mr. Hogby, who declines, for one reason or another, to pay these costs; and, for one reason or another, I am bound to say that in my opinion he is damn well right.

The application is dismissed.

27 July, 1938

NOTE: (1) His Lordship's second ground of complaint was later removed: and defended divorce suits (to the disgust of His Majesty's Judges) can be heard at Assizes. (2) The system of court fees remains, and has recently been laboriously considered by the Committee on Supreme Court Practice and Procedure (Chairman, Sir Raymond Evershed, Master of the Rolls), of which the editor is a humble member. This Committee were informed by the Lord Chancellor (see their Second Interim Report, 1951, Cmd. 8176) that 'The proposal that court fees should be entirely abolished would involve the abrogation of a principle which has been accepted by Parliament and the country for many generations, *viz.* that suitors in the Courts are properly required to bear some proportion of the costs of the machinery of the administration of justice. The taxpayer already contributes a substantial proportion of the costs, and the transference of the whole financial burden of the machinery (which would have to be not only for the Supreme Court, but for all other courts of law) would, we feel, involve questions of public finance which are far beyond the scope of the Committee's enquiry.' But they were permitted, and encouraged, to consider the question 'whether the Supreme Court Fees Order requires overhauling' and did so.

They found (p. 56) that 'in an average small action in the King's Bench Division, where the total bill of costs is in the neighbourhood of £200, court fees may be expected to account for about 6 per cent. of the total. In the case of larger actions, where the total bill of costs is greater, the percentage attributable to court fees is likely to be smaller, and in very big cases considerably smaller. It is obvious, therefore, that even the total abolition of court fees would bring no great relief to the litigant, and the degree of relief which we feel entitled to recommend can only be comparatively small. We cannot afford, however, to neglect any possible means of reducing the costs of litigation, by however small an amount, and being satisfied that some relief from court fees can be given to the litigant without injustice to the taxpayer we think that such relief should be given.'

Detailed recommendations were made: for which you must buy this fascinating Report. It is marked 1s. 9d. net. In other words, though a Government production, it is governed by one of those Retail Price Maintenance Agreements on which His Majesty's Ministers have recently frowned. And see *Rex* v. *Lambert* where a publican, to attract custom to his overtaxed house, sold stamps below the Government price, and without a licence.

(2) REX *v.* REINSTEIN

THE WIZARDRY CASE

THERE was a dramatic turn to the Palmistry trial to-day. Doctor Reinstein, the fashionable 'futuropath,' has appealed to Quarter Sessions against his conviction by the Burbleton magistrates as a rogue and vagabond under the Vagrancy Act, 1824, for 'pretending to tell fortunes by palmistry or otherwise.' The court was full of mink and pearls, for many of the doctor's Mayfair clients had come to see his final duel with the law. Lady Vague, the Hon. Mrs. Marsh-Mallow, and Mr. Edward Sonnet have already testified to the comfort they have received from his estimates of their character and forecasts of their future.

After a severe cross-examination by the Attorney-General, Mr. Mould rose to re-examine the doctor. He handed the witness a blue book:

Kindly turn to page 112. Do you see any predictions there?

Yes. It is stated here that at exactly 12.0 noon on September 1st the planet Venus will be over the meridian of Greenwich. The book also says that Venus will then be 41·2 minutes of arc below the celestial equator.

41·2 minutes? About 40 miles? That is fairly precise, is it not? What else do you find?

The book is full of predictions—300 pages of them. On page 148 we are told that on December 19th the planet Mars will pass less than 1 degree (42 minutes) South of Saturn.

Do you believe these predictions?

Certainly.

Have you the faintest idea how they are arrived at?

None.

The Chairman (Sir Philip Crow): What is this book, Mr. Mould?

Mr. Mould: The *Nautical Almanac*, milord, published by order of the Lords Commissioners of the Admiralty.

The Chairman: It is not illegal, is it, to predict the movements of the heavenly bodies?

Mr. Mould: No, milord. That is the extraordinary thing.

Counsel then handed to the prisoner a small black box, about the size of a cigar-box.

Kindly lift the lid of that box, Doctor.

The Doctor did so. A shrill soprano voice was heard, singing a melancholy song.

The Chairman: God bless my soul! What is this?

Prisoner: That is Gracie Fields, sir, singing 'Sally.'

He turned a small wheel and the voice filled the court.

The Chairman (shouting): WHAT—HAS—MISS—FIELDS—TO—DO—WITH—THIS—CASE?

Mr. Mould: MILORD—SHE—IS—AT—MANCHESTER.

The Chairman: BUT—IF—SHE—HAS—ANYTHING—TO—SAY—SHE—OUGHT—TO—BE—HERE. I—CAN'T—ALLOW—— WILL—YOU—STOP—THAT—FRIGHTFUL—NOISE?

(The prisoner closed the lid.)

Really, Mr. Mould! Perhaps you will now explain the purport of your examination?

Mr. Mould (to the prisoner): Do you believe that the sound emerging from that small box was the voice of Miss Gracie Fields singing at Manchester, 180 miles from this court?

Prisoner: In a sense, no. It does not seem to me to be possible. I cannot imagine how it is done. But I have to accept it, like other wonders I do not understand.

Mr. Mould glanced at his watch and said: Reduce the volume, please, and raise the lid again.

The Chairman (anxiously): Mr. Mould——!

A refined voice said: 'Here are the weather forecasts. Outer Hebrides . . .'

The Chairman: You need not go on with that, Mr. Mould. We see the point.

I have one more witness, milord. Call Ebenezer Mole.

When Mr. Mole, a rustic type, had been sworn, Mr. Mould

B

asked if the witness might be permitted to walk about the court. He carried a forked twig.

The Chairman (wearily): If you think it will help, Mr. Mould. You are not, I hope, going to call any performing bears?

No, milord.

The witness walked about, holding the twig in front of him. At the back of the court he halted and said: 'There be water below, dang Oi if there bean't.'

The Chairman: What *is* all this?

The witness is a water-diviner.

The Chairman: Yes, but—— Usher, *is* there any water there?

Usher: Yes, milord, the lavatories are just below.

The Chairman: Bless me! But I don't see—— Does the Crown wish to question this witness?

The Attorney-General: No, milord.

Mr. Mould: That concludes the case for the defence.

Milord, you will forgive, I hope, the unconventional methods I have been compelled to use in this case. My client is charged with 'pretending to tell fortunes by palmistry and otherwise with intent to deceive' under an Act of 1824. Only a hundred years before, in 1716, a woman and her child were hanged for witchcraft. Anyone in that century who had claimed to produce from a small box the voice of a woman singing 180 miles away would certainly have been hanged as well. Now we know better. But fragments of the old ignorance remain embedded in our laws: and with one such, I submit, we have to deal to-day. Our ancestors suspected and shrank from any person who did anything which they could not understand: for the conclusion was that the person was possessed by, or falsely claimed to possess, some supernatural power. We know now that many good things are done by mortal men which the rest of us are quite unable to do, explain, or even understand. How fantastic, how unbelievable, it is that a simple peasant with a forked hazel twig should be able to detect the presence of water, or minerals, under the ground! Yet this piece of wizardry is now so well accepted that my learned friend the Attorney-General did not think it worth while to cross-examine the witness Mole. Our fathers frowned, our law still frowns, on any claim to predict the future—especially if the prediction is said to depend upon the heavenly bodies.

The Judge: You mean all that stuff about being 'born under Libra,' with Venus in the ascendant, and so forth? It decides your character, they say.

Mr. Mould: Yes, milord.

The Judge: My gardener says you should always sow under a waxing moon. The full moon pulls the things out, he says, and you get a better quality.

Mr. Mould: Something of the sort, I believe, is now being taught in certain agricultural colleges.

The Judge: Is it indeed? Well, perhaps, the astrologers are not so far out. Bulbs and babies—much the same thing, I dare say.

Mr. Mould: Who knows, milord? Then there are the tides. Every year the Admiralty publishes elaborate tables predicting the height and the time of the tides at every port in the Kingdom, and these tables are founded on the movements of the sun and moon.[1] Then there are the weather reports——

The Chairman: The law distinguishes, does it not, Mr. Mould, between predictions of a general character and predictions concerning the future of an individual? You may say, 'There will be war next year,' but not 'Colonel X., you will go to war in January.'

Mr. Mould: The predictions I have mentioned, milord, are highly selective and particular—the weather in the Hebrides, the Isle of Wight, the Dogger Bank, and so forth. The tides at Southampton, the tides at Harwich. Venus will be in such-and-such a place at 12 noon. If it is lawful to predict the future of a particular planet——

The Chairman: Venus pays no fees—that is the difference. What have you to say about palmistry?

Mr. Mould: Palmistry, milord, is said to have existed in China

[1] Lord Mildew said in *Orient Line* v. *Port of London Authority* (1913): 'I never believed that the moon had anything to do with it.'

three thousand years before Christ, and is lawfully practised over vast areas of the earth to-day. The hand, the constant tool of man, could hardly fail to receive important imprints. The hand of the sailor, the clerk, the housewife (in these days), can be recognized by the amateur observer.

The Chairman: They say you can tell a male frog by his thumb.

Mr. Mould: If your Lordship pleases. To the expert, of course, the hand reveals mysteries which are beyond us, like those of radio and water-divining and astronomy. But my client, as he has said, does not rely on the palms only. He uses also all those other indications of character which help my learned friend to sum up a witness so successfully. On these he founds an estimate, a chart of behaviour, probable conduct in a probable future, so far as he can forecast it. 'Forecast' is the word he uses to his clients: and, like the weather-men, he admits that he may be wrong. But he pleads not guilty to the charge of 'pretending to tell fortunes.' Within the limits I have named, he says that he can and does tell fortunes—and is proud of it. In the light of what we have seen and heard to-day, can any of you be sure that that is a baseless claim?

The Attorney-General made a long speech. But the Doctor was acquitted.

31 October, 1951

NOTE: But see *Rex* v. *Oates* (1950), 2 A.C., a test-case, where a 'tipster' was charged as a 'rogue and vagabond' for 'napping' a horse called *Mameluke* to win the 3.30 at Sandown Park (a 'nap' meaning, according to the Crown, 'I predict with certainty that *Mameluke* will win'). The magistrates convicted on the ground that the prediction was not 'general,' but referred to an 'individual.' Moreover, the accused, in support of his prognostication, mentioned the hocks and other portions of *Mameluke's* anatomy, which, said the justices, put the affair in the domain of 'palmistry.' On appeal, Quarter Sessions confirmed the conviction. *Held*, in the Court of Appeal, (Wedderburn L.J. dissenting) that a horse, though an 'individual,' was not a man, and that his movements, as those of a star, might freely be predicted by anyone. The conviction was quashed. Wedderburn L.J. said: 'The point is not the subject, but the object, of the prophecy. Money passed. The prediction was erroneous. I can perceive small difference between saying "I see by your hand, Mrs. X., that you will be happy next year," and saying "I see by his hocks that the horse *Mameluke* will win to-day." Of the two assertions the second seems to me to be the more anti-social and difficult to justify.'

(3) INTEGRATED PRESS *v.* THE POSTMASTER-GENERAL

WHAT IS A NEWSPAPER?

(Before Mr. Justice Codd)

SITTING in the Vacation Court, his Lordship to-day gave judgment in *The Swim Girl* case. He said:

This is an unusual action. In form it is an application to make absolute a rule *nisi* vaguely in the nature of the old *mandamus* calling upon the Postmaster-General and the Newspaper Registry Office at Somerset House to show cause why they should not register *The Sunday Sensation* as a newspaper.

In these days, when so much is heard about the 'Freedom of the Press,' it is as well to remember that the proprietors and publishers of newspapers are still compelled to register (under the Newspaper Libel and Registration Act, 1881), though not, as in the first half of the reign of Queen Victoria, to deposit a sum of money when they do so. Further, since a newspaper counts as a 'book,' a copy (sometimes two) must be sent to the British Museum, the Bodleian Library and other statutory libraries, where they are received, no doubt, with ill-concealed delight by the librarians.

In return they enjoy certain special advantages. A newspaper 'registered at the General Post Office' may be despatched through the post at lower rates than ordinary communications or even 'printed papers.' Further (though this, I think, is not a statutory privilege), they are allowed to market their wares in the streets, through stationary or itinerant salesmen, and to advertise them by the making of loud cries, in a manner which would not be permitted to any other trade, except at a recognised market. It is odd, by the way, that our Parliament and people should take so strong an objection to the quiet negotiation of bets in a public street when they do not mind the loud selling of sensations, disasters and scandals in the same street.[1]

Now, for many years *The Sunday Sensation* has been registered as a newspaper both by Somerset House and the General Post Office. In the present year both have refused to do so on the sole and simple ground that *The Sunday Sensation* (with which is now incorporated *The Swim Girl*) is no longer a newspaper.

The proprietors reply, with indignation and surprise, (*a*) that their publication *is* a newspaper, and (*b*) that that question (whatever the correct answer) does not concern the two offices named, whose simple duty it is to register upon demand.

Let us consider the second point first. No doubt in the past the registration of *The Sunday Sensation*, as of *The Sunday Times*, has in fact been almost automatic. But is there any necessity or justification in law for saying that it must be automatic? I cannot think so. Suppose, for example, that someone were to put forward as a 'newspaper' a publication which consisted entirely of extracts from the Bible on the one hand, or of obscene pictures on the other. For different reasons both would be illegal. No one, surely, would suggest that either Somerset House or the Post Office was bound to register such sheets as newspapers simply because the proprietors gave to them that honourable name. It follows that registration is not a matter of right but of fact or reason, and that the authorities have a power to say, in certain cases, what is and what is not a newspaper. The two cases posited are, admittedly, extremes, but they indicate the kind of reasoning which should be applied to all cases on the wrong side of the borderline, and the task of determining where that borderline lies is very familiar to our courts of law and, in this affair, is by no means uncongenial to me.

I turn, then, to the question of fact. Assuming that some publications can rightly be described and registered as news-

---

[1] And see *Sabatini* v. *Sale*, where an organ-grinder, having been 'warned off' for annoyance, complained that his nerves were lacerated by the yelling of a newsvendor. The case was dismissed as frivolous.

papers, and some cannot, in which class ought the King's Courts to place *The Sunday Sensation* (and *Swim Girl*)?

'News' is a wide and generous term. *The Oxford English Dictionary* offers the following description (heading 2): 'TIDINGS: the report or account of recent events or occurrences, brought or coming to one as new information: new occurrences as a subject of report or talk.' It may include events of every kind and degree of importance, from the declaration of a war to the termination of a marriage. It may be of cosmic, continental, national, local or merely professional interest. The information that a new type of potato-chipper has been perfected is not less 'news' because it is exciting only to the readers of *The Fish Friers' Gazette*. But if, say, seventy per cent. not of one but of every issue of that paper were occupied by photographs of potato-chippers the question would arise whether *The Fish Friers' Gazette* had not ceased to be a newspaper in the proper sense and was now a mere circulating photograph album.

What applies to potato-chippers may be thought to apply with at least equal force to swim-girls. Let it be remarked at once that this Court has no objection to photographs of young ladies in bathing-dresses, as such. On the contrary, the Court enjoys them as much as ever. How about you, Sir Roger?

Sir Roger Wheedle, K.C.: Milord, I take *The Times*.

The Judge: How about Sundays?

Sir Roger: The Sunday Times, milord; and I try to keep up with the *Economist* and the *Bilious Weekly*.

The Judge: Well, well. Nor is the Court much impressed by the contention that the frequent contemplation of young ladies in bathing-dresses must tend to the moral corruption of the community. On the contrary, these ubiquitous exhibitions have so diminished what was left of the mystery of womanhood that they might easily be condemned upon another ground of public policy, in that they tended to destroy the natural fascination of the female, so that the attention of the male population was diverted from thoughts of marriage to cricket, darts, motor-bicycling and other occupations which do nothing to arrest the decline of the population. But the Court expresses no opinion on that. And, apart from that, the photographs appear to be socially beneficial—at all events they are beneficial to the Court. For at least the young ladies are radiantly happy, which is more than can be said of most of those whose doings are recorded in the papers. And whether they are poised upon a rock or diving-board, bounding into the ocean, or coyly teasing their companions in the water, it is evident that they are healthy and it is assumed that they possess or will acquire some skill in swimming. All this must surely provide a useful example to other young persons, and, in a country so much dependent on mastery of the sea, might even prove valuable for the defence of our shores.

But that is not the point in issue. The evidence, as I have already hinted, is that in the summer months some seventy per cent. of the space of *The Sunday Sensation* (and *Swim Girl*) is filled with blithe young ladies in similar but scanty costumes. Even in the winter the proportion does not fall by as much as might be expected, for swimming still continues in swimming-baths and tropical waters, and the new models for next year's costumes must of course be exhibited for the judgment of the public. All this may be admirable in its way: but, in any strict sense, in such proportions, can it be said to be 'news'?

It would be fair at this point to turn to the small remainder of the paper, for here perhaps may be found, though in miniature, the essential elements of a newspaper. What do we find? One witness unkindly said that the remainder of the paper consisted entirely of headlines and hysteria. The headlines are abnormally large (indeed, where it is thought necessary to employ headline-type an inch in depth to announce that a lady has been divorced, one wonders what would be required for the outbreak of a world war). But the messages below the headlines are printed in type abnormally small. There is evident here not merely a deficient sense of proportion but, I should say, an elementary technical blunder. For it is the purpose of the headline to attract attention to the full story below—it is, as it were, the label on the meat. But when the labels are so large and loud and numerous as here the general effect in the end must be distracting. The eye is dutifully prepared to accept the flaring invitation to the bigamy at Surbiton when it is diverted by another beacon, equally brilliant and alarming, to the latest banned book. But in the next column or page another scandal, not less distressing, again seduces the attention. And in each case the actual story is printed in type so small and difficult to read that any distraction is doubly powerful.

However, once more, that is not the question before the Court. Do the 'events and occurrences' thus presented, wisely or not, constitute news in such a proportion as to make the paper a newspaper? The weight of the evidence is against that view. No one has suggested that every newspaper should give an equally full and laborious account of all the major events and movements of the day, the work of Governments and Parliaments, the situation and relations of foreign governments, the achievements of art, literature and the sciences; nor, on the other hand, that any paper should be bound to ignore those painful but enjoyable stories of misfortune, scandal and corruption which are so large a part of the tale of mankind. But it was powerfully urged that a habitual concentration upon the latter, coupled with a habitual exclusion of the former, would raise a presumption so strong as to shift the onus of proof on to the complainant in these proceedings. It was said also by counsel for the Crown that, allowing for the many and desirable differences in the class and character of newspapers, every newspaper claiming privileges as such ought at least to offer to its readers some small scrap of authentic information on the most important of the events of the day, and, if possible, some modicum of helpful comment or guidance.

The head of an advertising firm said bluntly that in his opinion *The Sunday Sensation* (and *Swim Girl*) provided no such thing. That suited him; and that was why he used the paper. There were some good articles in it, but nothing you could call news. There were no leading articles at all. That was grand.

This piece of evidence, coming from one who had no axe to grind (whatever that may mean), was for me the last link in a solid and impressive chain. If I find for the Crown in this case the familiar cry will, no doubt, be heard that the liberties of the Press so hardly contested and finally won in the last century are being whittled away. That cry will here be wholly inappropriate. In the first place the liberties of the Press were won for the kind of Press that then existed, for organs of thought, of character and refinement. Most of our great papers deserve that description to-day; and one might censure the black sheep without casting a single shadow upon them. But, in the second place, there is no question here of tampering with anyone's liberties. The proprietors of this paper will still be at liberty to print and disperse their entertaining album of photographs and anecdotes, but they will not be permitted to call it a newspaper and so to enjoy the privileges attached to that name by the Crown and Parliament. I find for the Crown. The rule is discharged.

10 August, 1938

NOTE: See also *Cute Publications* v. *Rumble* (1951), 2 A.C., where it was held that registration had been rightfully refused to the *Daily Delight* on the ground that more than 50 per cent. of its space was given to 'comic strips,' advice on football pools and betting, and pictures of attractive women. 'To look at a page of "comic strips,"' said Rutt L. J., 'is to despair of Progress. They take us back to an age when man could only express himself by drawing crude pictures of animals on the walls of caves, or making marks in the sand or snow. It may be that this is the kind of entertainment the people desire and deserve, but clearly it does not merit the special privileges reserved for a "newspaper." We were told that a strip called "Jane" won the Election of 1945. The Court remains unimpressed.'

(4) GREENWICH WOMEN'S ROWING CLUB *v.* HADDOCK

WHAT IS A ROWING BOAT?

A POINT of high importance to mariners was discussed, if not decided, in the Admiralty Court to-day. The action arose out of a collision between a ladies' eight and a motor-boat navigated by Mr. Albert Haddock.

After a long learned argument the President, Sir Thomas Bowline, said:

This case raises a question which, so far as I know, has never come before a British court of law, and, but for the inconsiderate and loathsome conduct of the defendant, would not have troubled us now. But here it is, and it must be considered.

The question, simply put, is: 'What is a rowing boat?' What is the status of a rowing boat in the grand hierarchy of vessels known to the law; and what, in particular, are the duties of those who navigate or approach such a vessel in the open sea or upon tidal waters? (There is no doubt, by the way, that before the law a rowing boat is a 'vessel,' however much the description may shock the practical mariner.)

Now, in the Regulations for the Prevention of Collisions at Sea, one of the most celebrated, sound and vital codes of conduct in the English tongue, the relations and the duties (it would be wrong to say 'rights') of the various types of vessel are very clearly defined for almost every conceivable situation.

'A steam vessel,' for example, 'shall keep out of the way of a sailing vessel' where there is risk of collision (Article 20): and a steam vessel 'shall include any vessel propelled by machinery.' A sailing vessel which is close-hauled on the port tack shall keep out of the way of a sailing vessel which is close-hauled on the starboard tack (Article 17). Sailing vessels under way shall keep out of the way of fishing vessels (Article 26).

Other regulations direct what lights shall be carried by trawlers, pilot boats, and even rowing boats (Article 7).

In the Port of London River Bye-laws, which are additional to but not inconsistent with the General Regulations, there are special rules concerning lighters, barges, dredgers, vessels towing and towed, and so forth. Each class has its appointed signs and duties for all occasions, and under the Steering and Sailing Rules the master of any steam or sailing vessel who sights another knows at once (if he knows his business) which of the two has a duty to 'keep out of the way of' the other, if necessary by altering course, and which, on the other hand, should maintain her course and speed. But he does *not*, from the Rules at least, know what he ought to do if he sights a rowing boat 'approaching him so as to involve risk of collision': for except in the section governing lights, there is no mention of rowing boats, either in the International Regulations or in the Port of London River Bye-laws.

This singular omission, especially in a river which is the scene of so much oarsmanship, has long been the cause of wonder and dispute among the mariners: but good sense has hitherto kept the discussion out of the courts. It will be convenient now to consider the perverse behaviour by which the defendant has brought it here to-day.

The defendant, while navigating down Blackwall Reach on the ebb, on or about the Prime Meridian, saw a vessel rowed by eight ladies on his port bow. She was shaping a south-easterly course obliquely across the river, at about 6 knots, and was likely (if both vessels held on) to cross his bows at a short distance or to collide with him. Both vessels did hold on; there was a collision; the ladies were thrown into the water, and were extricated, one by one, by the defendant, a process which, he said in evidence, he greatly enjoyed. This deplorable comment, unfortunately, has no juridical significance, and the Court must reluctantly ignore it—that is, until the question of costs comes up.

The rowing club sued Mr. Haddock for negligent navigation causing the loss of their boat and some sickness among her

crew. Mr. Haddock put in the impudent defence that a
rowing boat counted as a steam vessel, and that in the circumstances the ladies ought to have kept out of his way
according to Article 19 of the Regulations. It is perfectly true
that if the eight had been in fact a steam vessel it would have
been her duty to stop or alter course so as to avoid a collision,
according to the old mnemonic lines:

> *If to your starboard red appear*
> *It is your duty to keep clear.*

But *is* a rowing boat a steam vessel within the meaning of
the Regulations? As I have said, they give us no clear guidance
in such a case. It is difficult to accept the contention of
defendant's counsel, ably though it was argued, that an eight-
oared rowing boat, at least, is 'a vessel propelled by machinery.'[1] The plaintiffs, on the other hand, say that a rowing
boat counts as a sailing vessel, and therefore the defendant
had an absolute duty to keep out of the way. One of the
defendant's witnesses, a very ancient mariner, went even
farther than the defendant. He said that there was a very
good reason why the rowing boat was not mentioned in the
steering regulations; that morally the rowing boat did not
exist, and practically the honest mariner was entitled to
behave as if it were not there. It was a nuisance; it was a
something nuisance; and, like the cat or dog, must look out
for itself.

I was not impressed by any of these opinions: and in the
absence of precise guidance I must look to the principles upon
which all these Regulations are founded. Why is it that the
steam vessel, however mighty, must give way, must alter

---

[1] But, with respect to the learned President, there is much to be said for
it. *The Oxford English Dictionary*, under heading 5 of 'Machine' gives:
'(*In Mechanics*) Any instrument employed to transmit force or to modify its
application. *Simple Machine*: one in which there is no combination of parts,
e.g. a lever. . . .' A quotation follows from D. Argill, *Reign Law*, ii (ed. 4),
90: 'A man's arm is a machine' (1866). Is not an eight-oared boat a vessel
propelled by eight 'simple machines'? See, *passim*, in the sporting sheets:
'The Cambridge boat moved like a machine.' Consider, too, the 'bathing-
machine' which was drawn by a horse.

course, must stop her engines, must go astern, in order to avoid a collision with a sailing vessel, however small? Because the steam vessel has the greater power and ease of manœuvre. She can turn aside (at least in the open seas, though not in the Thames) without effort or danger, where the sailing ship, at grips with wind and tide, can not. Might has its duties as well as its privileges, we are fond of saying: and this Regulation is one of the finest applications of it to be found in our written codes of conduct.

Now, if this be the principle, how is it to be applied to the present facts? How does an eight-oared boat, in power and progress, compare in fact with Mr. Haddock's motor vessel? On this point the defendant's evidence was clear, and I accept it. He says that his vessel is modestly equipped with two 9-horse-power engines and, being at least six tons (he does not seem to know exactly what his tonnage is), proceeds at most at about nine knots (with a good tide under him). Eight-oared boats, he says, whether driven by men or women, go past him with the utmost ease; and he reminded the Court that the University Boat Race, in a bad year, is rowed and won at the rate of about 12·75 land miles per hour. On these facts it seems impossible to say that the eight-oared boat (male or female) is a kind of Cinderella, requiring special privileges. She has more power than Mr. Haddock, not less; she draws very little water; she is steered by a skilled coxswain. In many situations she might well have more ease and power of manœuvre than Mr. Haddock's more solid and cumbrous craft; and in fact, in the present situation, there is no doubt that by stopping or altering course she could without difficulty have avoided the collision. All these considerations inclined me strongly to the view that Mr. Haddock ought to succeed.

But then, as counsel for the plaintiffs very properly reminded me, an eight-oared boat is not the only class of vessel 'under oars.' There is, for example, especially in London River, the great lighter, driving or drifting on the tide, and arduously steered by a single man with a single monstrous sweep. Here, it is obvious, Mr. Haddock, though he has eighteen horses only at his command, has the greater power of manœuvre and must, at his peril, keep out of the way.

Where are we, then? If I found my general rule upon the nature of the eight-oared boat it must prove inapplicable to the lighter 'under oars,' and *vice versa*; and between the two lies the ordinary small boat, propelled by oars or sculls, which, according to circumstances, may or may not be easily manœuvred. It is now, perhaps, a little more clear why the authors of the Regulations said nothing about vessels under oars. It was too much for them.

Like them, I decline to pronounce any general answer to the problem. Practically, on the facts of the case, I think that Mr. Haddock should succeed. But, morally speaking, I should be reluctant indeed to come down on the side of this ungallant mariner and contumacious litigant. Fortunately, the Regulations provide me with an honourable exit from this dilemma. I refer to Article 27. It is one of the merits of this austere code that it confers no rights upon anyone—only duties. Even the mariner whose duty it is in a given situation to maintain his course and speed, the other vessel giving way, is not thereby relieved of responsibility. For Article 27 ingeniously and admirably provides that he may still be wrong. That Article is headed 'SPECIAL CIRCUMSTANCES,' and says:

> 'In obeying and construing these Rules, due regard shall be had to all dangers of navigation and collision, and to any special circumstances which may render a departure from the above Rules necessary in order to avoid immediate danger.'

That Article, in my judgment, is applicable in the present case, even assuming, as I do not in terms assume, that the plaintiffs were, in the first instance, at fault. I find therefore that Mr. Haddock was possibly right but practically wrong. Judgment, and every kind of costs, for the plaintiffs.

6 November, 1940

NOTE: It is now the general opinion among sea-faring men that this case was wrongly decided. For one thing, under the Port of London Regulations, a vessel crossing the river, even a ferry, should keep out of the way of a vessel passing up or down the river. The ladies' boat was *crossing the river*. But this point does not appear to have been taken. The ladies (see the print in the National Maritime Museum) were attractive, and attended the trial.

(5) HADDOCK *v.* SILKWORM

BOOKS INTO BOMBS

MR. JUSTICE MOUSE, sitting without a jury, to-day gave judgment in this libel action. He said:

This is a suit for damages for defamation brought by Mr. Albert Haddock, an author, against Mr. Andrew Silkworm, head of the well-known multiple stores.

The circumstances of the complaint are unusual. The defendants prominently exhibited a book by the plaintiff in the window of one of their stores in one of the principal streets of the Metropolis, the Strand. In the ordinary way most authors would be glad and grateful to have the attention of the public drawn to their works in such a place and manner. But the window in question was devoted to a praiseworthy display in aid of a 'Salvage Drive' at that time being conducted by the Ministry of Supply. It contained a great number of old tooth-paste containers and milk-bottle tops, a pile of rags, a heap of waste paper, and other objects designed to show the people how they can contribute to the Allied cause by salving and surrendering any waste matter suitable for the making of munitions of war. And in the middle of the window were placed five or six books as a kind of centre-piece to the entire display. One of these books was by George Eliot, another by Lord Lytton, one by M. André Maurois, one by an eighteenth-century philosopher, and two by Mr. Haddock and another modern author.

Not far off, in Trafalgar Square, the centre of the 'Salvage-Drive,' bands were playing, flags flying, and public men from time to time were making speeches. Leaflets were distributed explaining in some detail the kind of scrap and waste matter the good citizens should surrender, to what processes it would be subjected, and what sort of munitions of war it would make or help to make. Four milk-bottle tops, he was told, will make one cartridge-cap plug. Three comic papers make two 25-pounder shell cups. One daily newspaper makes three 25-pounder shell cups. And six old books make one mortar-shell carrier.

Waste paper, the leaflet continues—and it seems clear that old books surrendered as salvage fall into the category of waste paper—is sent to the pulping-mills, where it is thrown into a stream of hot water which carries it to the breaker-beater. This machine contains revolving knives which shred the paper and reduce it to a coarse brown pulp with a consistency like that of pease-soup.

Sir Ambrose Wett: Milord, with great respect, in fairness to my clients, the consistency, in fact, is described as being like that of *porridge*.

The Judge: Thank you, Sir Ambrose. I beg your pardon. The pulp then passes on to the sand-trap channels, where dirt and grit are deposited—and so on.

Now, it will be at once conceded by any sensitive mind that an author is likely to feel pain at the thought of the children of his brain being torn to pieces with revolving knives and reduced to a coarse brown pulp with a consistency like that of porridge. The assurance, however, that six of his books will go to the manufacture of one mortar-shell carrier and so contribute to the destruction of tyrants must be some comfort to any patriotic writer. Indeed, to do him justice, the plaintiff told the Court that, if that were all, he would no more shrink from a necessary sacrifice than the rest of his gallant fellow-countrymen.

Question 1,453: Would it be fair to say that at this crisis in your country's fortunes, when all classes are making sacrifices, you begrudge your books to the national defences?

Witness: No, Sir Ambrose. If the supply of mortar-shell carriers should ever fall short of the nation's requirements, I would willingly sit down and write more books to make good the deficiency.

The Court commended him.

But that, he says—and there is a good deal of evidence to support him—is not quite all. There seems to be some confusion of purpose among His Majesty's Departments in the matter of books. The plaintiff told the Court that he himself has more than once been desired by persons in authority to make appeals to the public to give up books, not for the pulping-machine but for the entertainment and refreshment of our soldiers and sailors in distant parts; and special arrangements were made for the collection and distribution of such books. The supply of new books is sharply limited by the shortage of paper, and therefore any old book of good quality acquires a new importance. A simultaneous injunction to throw all old books into the dust-bin with the tooth-paste containers does suggest, at first sight, the presence of divided counsels among those who govern us, a suggestion which must always be wounding to the loyal subject. And, as the plaintiff observed, if the needs of the nation demand the general destruction of old books it would surely be administratively simpler to requisition public libraries and second-hand bookshops *en bloc*. It is believed, for example, that there are many volumes at such institutions as the Bodleian Library and the British Museum whose 'practical' value would be questioned by many.

We were glad, therefore, to hear the evidence of an official of the Ministry of Supply. He said that the policy of the salvage authorities was not, in fact, the wholesale destruction of books. The books received are 'sorted out' and those considered suitable are sent to the fighting forces and the Mercantile Marine. This process is called Book Recovery. Who makes the selection of books to survive and upon what grounds, or what proportion of the books surrendered go to the troops and what to the porridge-makers was by no means clear. Some may think that a somewhat sinister form of Government censorship of thought has come into being; for what man is fitted to say what books are 'suitable' for his fellow-men? And is there any reason to suppose that persons skilled in the general business of salvage have any special aptitude for literary criticism? Some may be of a narrow way of thought and condemn to the breaker-beater works of lively fancy like the plaintiff's: others, appointed to their posts without due examination of character, may despatch to our innocent fighting men works which none of us would care to see them enjoy.

But these questions, say the plaintiff's counsel, are only the background of his case. For whether or not the Ministry's policy of Book Recovery be wisely conceived and carried out, *there is no mention of it in the defendants' window*. The books, including the plaintiff's, are not displayed there as examples of the kind of work which the citizen, however much he prizes them, should cheerfully surrender for the comfort of the fighting men. At least, if that is in the mind of the defendants, it nowhere appears. They are displayed in the company of old rags and tooth-paste containers; they are displayed, according to him, as *ejusdem generis* with such articles: and the message, for any ordinary and reasonable citizen, must be that the plaintiff's book is fit only to be torn to pieces and converted into a brown porridge. The defendants, while they deny the innuendo, say that it is a compliment to any author in time of war to suggest that a book of his may make the sixth part of a mortar-shell container. The plaintiff replies that though that might be held a compliment by those who provided the paper and the binding, it would not add anything to his reputation as a writer. On the whole I think that he has sustained this part of his case. If the defendants mean to say: 'This is the sort of book you should give to the troops' they should say so clearly. What they have said, if they have said anything, is: 'This book is no better than an old tooth-paste container.'

But then, I have to ask myself, have they, in effect, said anything? The plaintiff's doctrine of *ejusdem generis* would carry us rather far. Many small traders sell books whose main business is not the selling of books, stationers, and so forth: and this must be 'good,' I presume, 'for trade.' I asked the plaintiff:

Question 2,001: Would you object to seeing your books exposed for sale with note-paper, blotting-paper, ink-stands, and typewriters?

Witness: No, milord. The more the merrier.

Question 2,002: Then, to take, perhaps, a fanciful case: suppose that a greengrocer chose to sell books, and exhibited your works for sale in the same window as his fruit. Would you complain that this was as much as to say that your books were no better than a cabbage or vegetable marrow?

Witness: No, milord, I suppose not.

On that frank answer, I am afraid, the plaintiff's case must be held to have foundered: and I find for the defendants. If it be asked why I spent so much time on the first part of the case, the answer is that I enjoyed it.

30 June, 1943

(6) HADDOCK *v.* MOLE

MR. JUSTICE CODD to-day delivered a considered judgment in the Orange Globes Case.
His Lordship said:

The plaintiff in this enthralling dispute is a Mr. Albert Haddock, who, although a mariner, is solicitous for the safety of the pedestrian ashore. He has assured the Court that he brings this action as a 'test' case for the guidance of all road-users, and does not in fact desire to receive for his own benefit the very substantial sum of damages which has been delicately suggested by his counsel. This somewhat improbable story is no concern of the Court, whose only business is to ascertain the truth of the facts in dispute and the law, if any, which applies to them.

The plaintiff, whose evidence, though unconventionally delivered, I take to be trustworthy, was crossing the Strand at one of the official 'pedestrian crossings' instituted by Regulations made under the Road Traffic Act, 1934. These crossings were the invention of a Minister of Transport who, after many years of increasing slaughter on the roads, formed the new and startling opinion that the safety and comfort of pedestrians were of at least equal importance as the impatience of those who were fortunate enough to travel by car: and, though it is not for the Court to look behind an Act of Parliament to any personality, we were informed that they will always be gratefully associated with the name of a Mr. Hore-Belisha.

Now, the duty of any driver approaching such a crossing is defined in the Regulations as follows: 'He shall, *unless* he can see that there is no foot-passenger there, proceed at such a speed as to be able, if necessary, to stop before reaching such crossing.' So that at these crossings the visible foot-passenger, at least, has a statutory right to life and limb.

But, for the Regulations to be effective, it was necessary that the crossing as well as the foot-passenger should be distinguishable by the motor-driver. For at other points, it is generally understood, the motorist is entitled to mow the foot-passenger down in the usual way. Therefore, they were marked by two rows of studs on the carriage-way, and, at each end, by a post painted alternately in black and white and surmounted by a globe of a distinctive orange colour, reminding the romantic of a harvest moon.

Unfortunately, in the years 1940 and 1941, many of these orange globes were destroyed by enemy action: others were removed or shattered by the impulsive soldiery of other lands, or by that type of indigenous citizen which delights to place unwanted perambulators in the emergency water-supply tanks thoughtfully provided against the burning of the capital.

It was by such a crossing, clearly indicated, that is, by the posts and the studs but not by orange globes, that Mr. Haddock lawfully elected to cross the Strand. He used, he assured the Court, all due consideration towards the drivers of motors, who in such a thoroughfare are not without anxieties of their own. With many other pedestrians, he patiently permitted about thirty vehicles to rush by, and when at last he stepped on to the carriage-way, raising his hand by way of additional warning, the nearest vehicles, he says, were not less than seventy-five yards away. Two of them bore on notwithstanding, the drivers laughing heartily, and at such a speed that the plaintiff was compelled to retreat in haste and ignominy to the pavement. A little later he made a second attempt, again, he says, with all due caution and consideration. This time the defendant was at the wheel of the leading vehicle; and he too continued on his course without slackening speed. Mr. Haddock, fortunately, was able to preserve his life, and to gain the 'refuge' by a sudden swift leap upward and forward, 'in the manner', to use his own vivid phrase, 'of an elderly chamois.' But life is not everything, and the exceptional effort severely aggravated a leg injury sustained elsewhere, which otherwise might not have troubled him much.

What was the trouble, Mr. Haddock? You used a long word I never met before.

Mr. Haddock: My Lord, I tore the gastrocnemious muscle, at the back of the calf.

The Judge: Just so. Mr. Haddock's own impression, he said, was 'that the car passed underneath him,' possibly an exaggeration. It is clear at least that for the safety of the plaintiff, lawfully 'there,' it was necessary for the defendant to stop before he reached the crossing, and that he did not stop, and, moreover, that he was unable to stop, according to the Regulations.

But, says Mr. Haddock, the defendant heaped insult upon injury; for as he whizzed away he shouted back *'Can't you see there ain't no orange balls?'*

This impudent plea he actually maintained, though with less and less conviction, at the hearing of the action. The plea is that the absence of the orange globes deprives the Regulation of effect and the crossing of consideration. But there are still the studs and the black-and-white posts. And even if such a suggestion had any practical or ethical validity, it would not, clearly, assist a driver who recognizes the posts sufficiently to remark that they support no orange globes.

Further, unfortunately for the defendant, the sly excuse has been anticipated by those in authority, and the Regulations have been so amended as to make it plain that the driver's duties are the same whether orange globes are visible or not. The defendant says that he did not know of that amendment; but he has been driving for a very long time, and it is his duty, at his peril, to know the law. None the less, it is for consideration whether, for the benefit of impetuous drivers and their victims, some additional sign, as prominent as the orange globe though less expensive, should not soon be provided at these crossings.

For they are valuable; they should be used by the walker, and respected by the driver. And when I say 'respected,' I

mean respected fully, in letter and in spirit. The walker's
right at these crossings is not a mere right to escape with his
life, after a moment of fear, by leaping into the air 'like an
elderly chamois' or mountain goat. It is a right to proceed
across the road without anxiety at a normal pace, or even, if
he be infirm or elderly, at a slow pace; and if motor-cars are
compelled thereby to go slow or even stop, so much the
better. The more cars stopped or slowed the less work for the
doctor and the undertaker. That is the sad and sobering fact.
On every day of 1943 three hundred and thirty-five persons
were killed or injured on the roads of England and Wales. For
the month of December the figure was 394. Only 850 fewer
persons were killed in 1943 than in 1938, when the motor-
vehicles were immensely more numerous. There is, I know, a
notion current that those who dart about at high speed are
exhibiting their loyalty to the cause of the United Nations and
somehow assisting that cause to victory. This is not necessarily
so; and very strong evidence will have to be produced in this
Court before that easy assumption is accepted. The defendant
must pay the plaintiff £5,000 damages; and in my opinion he
should be executed. For reasons, however, which are hidden
from the Court, the Legislature is more concerned for his life
than he is for others.

16 February, 1944

NOTE: See also Mr. Haddock's verse-translation of paragraph 37 of
the Highway Code:

Pedestrian Crossings

37. 'Look out for pedestrian crossings. Learn and observe the
Regulations relating to them. (*See* p. 28.)'

> Here are the beacons, here the studded ground
> Where bodies must on no account be found.
> Our duties here the Traffic Laws define:
> You should be 'stoppable' before the line;
> But rare indeed, I much regret to say,
> The motor-drivers who approach that way.

Call us 'jay-walkers' if we rove elsewhere:
But use us kindly if we walk with care.
Can you expect a chap to play the game
If he is chased and chivvied just the same?
It's not enough, sir, not to do us harm:
We have a right to cross without alarm.
So do not whizz an inch behind my back;
For all you know I'll have a heart-attack.
We, for our part, must make our purpose clear,
Not loiter on the studs, nor stop to jeer.
If both of us have gumption and goodwill
The population will be higher still.

(7) HADDOCK *v.* TOMKINS AND ISAAC

WHAT IS A REACTIONARY?

MR. JUSTICE ROTE, summing up to the jury in this case, said:

This action for defamation is brought by Mr. Albert Haddock, a Member of Parliament, against the editor of a journal called the *Tumbril* and a writer who contributes to that paper over the pseudonym of 'Culex.'[1] As the hearing of the case proceeded the fact emerged that both the defendants were Members of Parliament also, and that the true name of Culex was Isaac—the Member for Bottlehithe. It might well be thought, therefore, that the dispute could have been settled at less expense in the Chamber, or even the Smoking-room, of the House of Commons, by one of those brisk and lively exchanges of abuse which clear the air so quickly and delight the populace so much. The plaintiff, however, has an answer to that, which I consider it is my duty to impress upon the jury. He says that if the second defendant, the writer 'Culex,' who, as he says, attacked him, had used his proper name he, Mr. Haddock, would not have considered this action at law necessary or justifiable. For, he says, it is an honourable tradition of the House of Commons that its Members, however much they may disagree with each other, or dislike each other, owe to each other certain decencies of behaviour. Any Member is entitled, within the rules of procedure and deportment, to say what he likes about another Member.[2] But that Member is entitled, and indeed expected, to make a reply if he has one. So highly valued is the right of reply that the courteous custom is for Member A to give notice to Member B that he intends to make an attack upon him in the House, so

[1] A gnat.
[2] He must not 'make a personal charge' or 'impute motives.'

that B may have the opportunity to be in his place and defend himself or his policy. And even when the attack is casual and unpremeditated Member B is still not without remedy. 'Suppose, for example,' the plaintiff said, 'that the defendant, speaking in debate, suggested in an unrehearsed parenthesis that I was an embezzler, a "Fascist," a vested interest, a rodent operative—or whatever might be the favourite insult of the moment. I could at once interrupt him and deny that I was an embezzler or a Fascist. Or I could bide my time and later, if I caught the Speaker's eye, I could answer the accuser in a speech. Failing that, if the charge were serious enough, I could ask for and obtain a special opportunity for a "personal explanation" in which I could assure the House that, however much I looked like a vested interest, I was not one in fact. Or, failing that, I could accost the defendant in the Smoking-room and say in a friendly manner, "Look here, old boy, what nonsense is this? You know perfectly well that I am not a rodent operative. Please do not say this again." Or I could approach him, less politely, in the corridor, and say "Sir, you are erroneous. If you do not apologize I shall knock your block off." None of these remedies, however, is open to me when I am attacked by a fellow Member writing an account of proceedings and personalities in Parliament under a false name: for the simple reason that I do not know who he is. For all I know, the gentleman for whom I am buying liquid refreshment in the Smoking-room is the same one who has just pseudonymously described me as an embezzler or vested interest. If I knew who the writer was I should be able to tell how much the accusation was prompted by prejudice or venom, and could expose in Parliament or in public the presence of these motives. Not knowing who he is, I have no remedy of a Parliamentary character, and outside Parliament I can only write to the journal: but my letter will not be displayed as prominently as the accusation, and at the end of my letter "Culex" in a slippery footnote will have the last word. This is not good enough: and therefore I have gone to law, chiefly to ascertain the real name of "Culex," and also to make a formal protest against the growing custom by which Members of Parliament, over high-sounding bogus Latin names[1], criticize their fellow——' At this point I stopped the witness, for the Court has nothing to do with the somewhat complicated niceties of Parliamentary behaviour. I mention the matter only because it may be relevant to the question of damages, and in case you have been influenced by the suggestion that this is one of those actions which 'ought never to have been brought.' I do not think it is.

What the defendant 'Culex,' or Isaac, wrote about the plaintiff was that he was 'a reactionary.' At the close of the plaintiff's case the defendant's counsel asked me to say that there was no case to go to the jury, on the ground that the word 'reactionary' was incapable of bearing a defamatory meaning. The dictionary is not of much assistance upon this point—'*Reaction*—retrograde tendency, especially in politics, whence "reactionary."' A 'retrograde tendency' can only mean a tendency to go back. Well, many wise and patriotic persons think that we should go back, after the war, to some form of League of Nations, to normal lighting in the streets, to Free Trade: but no one describes them as reactionaries. Russia shows a tendency to go back into Poland, and has done so for a long time: but all men know that she is the most 'progressive' of nations. That the *intention* of the defendants is offensive there can be little doubt in the minds of any who heard their evidence or have read their writings: for 'the forces of reaction,' 'reactionary government,' and so on, occur in every paragraph, and they are invariably applied to persons or parties of whom they disapprove. But I have to inform you that intention is not the whole matter. The question is: Does the word tend to bring the plaintiff into hatred, ridicule or contempt? Will the ordinary reasonable man think the worse of him?

I had no doubt about my answer. This is one of many expressions which, colourless and even meaningless at first, have been developed into recognized terms of abuse by sloppy writers, prejudiced thinkers and powerful evangelists. The ordinary reasonable man has been trained to shudder away from a 'reactionary' as he does from a 'vested interest,' though he may have no clear notion of the nature of either.

I therefore directed that the case must proceed; and the question you now have to answer is: 'Is the plaintiff a "reactionary" in any sense, or not?'

The evidence of the defendants here becomes important. According to them, the main mark of a 'reactionary' is that he is opposed to progressive changes; and by the word progressive they mean changes which they themselves desire. It is necessary to emphasize the latter point, because some of the changes they advocate might almost be thought to have 'a retrograde tendency.' A reactionary, they said, would leave the House of Lords as it is. One of them would replace it by an elected Second Chamber; the other would abolish it and put nothing in its place. To adopt Single Chamber government, it may be remarked, would, without doubt, historically, be a retrograde step, moving back towards the most primitive stages of political life; but to this witness the change would be 'progressive.'

The plaintiff, on his own record and opinions, was clear and credible. He entered Parliament, he said, to advocate certain changes, in his view, 'progressive,' a long list of which was given in his election address.[1] Most of these he had in fact advocated since his election, by speech or otherwise, some with

[1] The laws of divorce, drink, betting, libel, Sunday entertainments, income-tax, entertainment-tax, and much besides. And see the anecdote in Haddock's *My Life and Letters*:

'Three days after I made a speech against the Fascists my house was burgled. Or, rather, my study was burgled. No other room was touched, and nothing, I believe, was taken. Even an envelope full of Treasury notes was left. But all my files and drawers were emptied, and all my political papers scattered on the floor. I formed two theories about this felony. One was that it was a political burglar, seeking ammunition for blackmail. The other was that it was an ordinary respectable burglar who, for some queer reason of his own, began at the study. He pulled out the files and read in swift succession "Divorce—Adultery—Cruelty—Insanity—Connivance—Collusion—Conduct Conducing—Nullity—Drink—Betting—Adultery," cried, "What sort of place am I in?" and ran screaming from the house.'

success. He could hardly recall a single speech he had made in Parliament which had not been designed to produce a change of some kind or another. In nearly every instance the condition of things at which he aimed was one which had never existed in these islands before: so it could not be said that his proposals had a retrograde tendency; and therefore they must be progressive. He did not choose to confine himself to the particular matters which were dear to the hearts of the defendants; but there were quite enough people doing that; and in any case it was a free country. Finally, he said that he had just completed a detailed scheme for the renaming of the stars. Was that the action of a reactionary?

The jury found for the plaintiff, with damages of £10,000.

22 March, 1944

NOTE: This case had a powerful effect. The 'bogus Latin names' are now much less numerous: and most Members of Parliament who write critical accounts of Parliamentary debates now do so openly, and creditably, over their own names.

(8) FESTER v. THE KING; FESTER v. PHILPOTT, RORY AND COMPANY LTD.; FESTER v. PLATT

THE 'LAW OF THE LAND'
(*Before Mr. Justice Cheese*)

HIS LORDSHIP, giving judgment in these important proceedings to-day, said:

Mr. Ambrose Fester, the plaintiff in these three suits, which, for convenience, have been taken together, is at least to be congratulated on his pertinacity, and he is to be assured at once that he has the sympathy of the Court, though, as Lord Mildew said in *Glass against the Metropolitan Water Board*, 'Sympathy pays no costs.'

The facts are these. Mr. Fester, a patriotic citizen, 'invalided' out of the Army, was employed by Messrs. Philpott, Rory and Company as an inspector at their important factory. It is admitted that he was a good and skilful servant and received what some would call, insanely, a 'sizeable' salary.

A Mr. Rice, another inspector, but a Government official, and not a member of the firm, addressed to the firm a letter which Mr. Fester was asked to sign to show that he had read it.

The letter began thus: '*Recent circumstances have created a chronological coincidence of two correlated occurrences calling for immediate comment.*'

Except that the author of this communication is fond of the letter 'C' the Court can form no clear opinion of its significance. Mr. Foster, a keen follower, as he told us in the box, of the good Mr. Haddock, took, in his own words, a 'dim view' of it, and wrote to the Government inspector as follows:

'SIR—In reply to your letter regarding Wip Valves, I suggest that you omit the ridiculous blank phraseology and state what you wish to convey in plain English.'

The 'blank' represents an expression which, while not often

D

used in drawing-rooms, even to-day, is familiar to all men with Service experience, is not blasphemous, or sexually indecent, and, in short, in my opinion, is no more than a vivid vulgarity.

Mr. Fester was then called before the general manager of his firm and invited to apologize to Inspector Rice. He refused. He was at once dismissed from his office.

Such is the reward, in the sphere of influence of Government Departments, of an independent mind and a respect for the English language.

Mr. Fester, however, was familiar with the long and, on the whole, honourable history of British justice. He knew that the first word is not always the last: and he appealed, in due form, to the local Appeal Board.

Now, under the Essential Works (General Provisions) Order, the purpose of which, the Court presumes, was to secure the highest possible efficiency in the factories and workshops of the nation in time of war, a man cannot, in effect, leave his employment without permission, and an employer, without permission, cannot summarily dismiss a man except for 'serious misconduct.'

I should mention in passing that the local Appeal Boards were at one time presided over by members of the legal profession, a wise arrangement, but we are informed that already, at the date of the proceedings in question, the Ministry of Labour had decided, and decreed, that no lawyer should sit on these tribunals. This is but one more illustration of a tendency and practice which must be deplored by all thinking men, the exclusion from affairs of justice of persons schooled in the arts and manners of justice. In passing, may I say, it surprises me that the Attorney-General, who appears for the Crown in this case, has been unable to use his persuasive powers to prevent or modify such arrangements.

Sir Anthony Slatt, K.C.: Milord, I have to obey orders, like others.

The Judge: Yes, but you are the head of the Bar: and the Ministry of Labour, I should have thought, would pay some attention to you as a trade union leader, if nothing else. However, all this, the Court supposes, is a sample of the fruits of 'the Century of the Common Man.' But, much as we admire within due limits the Common Man, and the Average Man, and the Man in the Street, and even that repellent figment of the jurist's imagination, the Reasonable Man, we own that in any medical or legal trouble we should rather commit ourselves to the care of a professional adviser than to any of these well-meaning but uninstructed amateurs.

In this case the worthy (but lay) chairman of the Appeal Board, and his colleagues, had to answer this question. Did the conduct of the plaintiff amount to 'serious misconduct'?

In the Order there is no definition of 'serious misconduct' (nothing to cause surprise in an enactment devised by a Government Department). But that omission would not dismay a trained lawyer, who would turn with confidence to the Common Law. And indeed the case-law is clear. Deliberate disobedience to orders, gross neglect of work, and so on, justify instant dismissal. But the theory that a boyish impertinence, or even an adult insult, to a Government official not in the same employ will justify instant dismissal is not supported by any recorded decision of any of His Majesty's Judges.

Of what avail is it, however, to quote the Common Law in proceedings where no trained lawyer is permitted either to sit among the judges or to represent the litigant or accused person? The Chairman, in this case, on being reminded that the Order did not define 'serious misconduct,' held himself entitled to put his own interpretation upon the phrase. Mr. Fester's appeal was rejected; and he is now employed at half his former wage, in a position where his technical accomplishments are not being used, and cannot be used, for the benefit of the nation.

In these circumstances Mr. Fester has come to the King's Courts for justice, or failing that, as he frankly said, to advertise his wrongs and the system which produced them.

The first writ which the young victim impulsively discharged was against Messrs. Philpott, Rory and Company for wrongful dismissal. This suit cannot be entertained for a moment, for the local Appeal Board has decided that the dismissal was rightful, and by the quaint provisions of the Order, approved by Parliament, there is no appeal from their decision.

Then he proceeds against Mr. Platt, his general manager, for slander. Well, Mr. Platt, it is true, informed the Appeal Board that the plaintiff had been guilty of serious misconduct. If there had been any evidence of malice I should have ruled that this bizarre tribunal was not a Court of Law and therefore that there was no absolute privilege for statements made before it. But I found no evidence of malice. The wretched Mr. Platt said simply that the Government Department concerned was now his only customer and therefore he had to do as he did to defend the honour and soothe the feelings of its wounded inspector, Mr. Rice. It is no part of my duty to comment upon such a state of affairs; but, if it were, I confess that I should discharge that part of it with alacrity and enjoyment.

Lastly, the injured youth, with touching faith in the ancient bulwarks of the British Constitution, has asked the Court for a declaration that the treatment he has received is contrary to the provisions of Chapter 29 of Magna Carta. It is perfectly true that in that famous Chapter 'we,' that is, the Crown, undertake, among other things, that 'we will not proceed against a freeman, nor condemn him but by lawful judgment of his peers, or by the law of the land.' But I am surprised and saddened to learn that there is any of the King's subjects so innocent as to suppose that these words have any practical significance to-day. Hardly anyone is condemned by his peers in these times, except such malefactors as are sensible enough to go in for murder or incest, and the 'law of the land' is regarded by most of our rulers as a kind of joke, to be evaded or excluded. In this case, as we have seen, the practitioners of the 'law of the land' were deliberately kept away, and the law itself was not even considered by the tribunal. But what can I do? This is the work of Parliament, supporting a despotic Executive, for the sake of a just war. Magna Carta, I regret to say, is dead 'for the duration,' at least; and only supreme exertions will renew its life at the termination of hostilities.

But there are still alive some remnants of our ancient rights and principles. It is not for me to advise the plaintiff or correct his solicitors. But I should have thought, without having studied the various Orders that govern us now, that it might still be possible to apply to the High Court for the issue of one of the prerogative writs in the nature of *mandamus* or *certiorari*, calling upon the local Appeal Board to show cause why they acted as they did and to justify their proceedings according to the still indestructible principles of natural, and even British, justice. That, no doubt, is a highly improper, and perhaps erroneous, suggestion: and I withdraw it at once.

I must, with regret, dismiss all the plaintiff's suits, and perhaps that will teach him to bother about the English language. Costs, however, to be paid by everybody, except Mr. Fester.

18 April, 1945

NOTE: His Lordship's hint was taken. A writ of *mandamus* did issue. The Appeal Board were torn to pieces by a strong court (Rammer L. C. J., Codd J., and Plush J.), and Mr. Fester was restored to his office.

(9) THE CORPORATION OF BURBLETON *v.* STANISLAVSKI

HOW FREE IS A FREEMAN?

MR. JUSTICE PLUSH to-day gave judgment in this unusual action which raises a question of interest to many townships at the present time. His Lordship said:

In this action the Corporation of Burbleton City are proceeding—reluctantly, as they have assured us, and we can well believe—against Marshal Stanislavski, the distinguished commander who has done so much for the cause of the Allied Nations in Eastern Europe. So sensible of his deeds and services were the people of Burbleton that they decided to confer upon him the Freedom of Burbleton. Accordingly, in a moving ceremony this year, the young Marshal was made an honorary Freeman of the Borough. There was a banquet; there were noble speeches; there was a procession, during which the excited citizens swarmed affectionately about the Marshal's car.

These emotions had scarcely subsided when, to the surprise and delight of the citizens, it was announced that the Marshal proposed to take up his residence in the first city to make him a freeman. Burbleton is by the sea, the Marshal is fond of swimming and boating; and in his own country, it appears, even a Marshal is subject to so many restraints and restrictions that the status of a freeman (unknown in his own land) made a very practical appeal to him. The grateful citizens purchased and presented to the Marshal a fine freehold mansion beside the sea; and there he resides.

Unfortunately, at no stage was it made clear to anyone or by anyone exactly what the privileges of a freeman are, which is indeed the question the Court has now to answer. Some light,

but not much, emerges from a study of the Honorary Freedom
of Boroughs Act, 1885. It is there laid down that persons of
eminence may be made Honorary Freemen of a Borough,
with a proviso that the persons so distinguished shall not be
entitled to a share in the produce or the proceeds of a sale of
any property or stocks belonging to the Corporation.

This purely negative information does not lead us very far.
Counsel for the plaintiffs has urged persuasively that the word
'honorary' is equivalent to 'formal,' that the whole affair is no
more than a symbolic courtesy and that no substantial
privileges are in fact or law conferred by it. The Court rejects
this view. We are satisfied that the word 'honorary' is used in
distinction from the old, and now forbidden, practice by which
it was possible to purchase the status of a freeman. Further,
putting the best construction, as we feel bound to do, on the
acts of a municipal corporation, we decline to assume that this
and other bodies can have performed with so much pomp and
circumstance an act that was practically meaningless.

Sir Roger Wheedle, K.C. (for the Corporation): Milord, if I may
—with great respect—I think my clients might reasonably
take exception to the expression 'meaningless.' The public
display of goodwill, the generous refreshment, the illuminated
address, the casket——

The Judge: Yes, yes, Sir Roger. But what I said was 'practically' meaningless. That, at all events, was the view taken
by the Marshal, who argued simply that a freeman must be
more free than one who was not a freeman, especially if he
was made free with so much ceremony and emotion.

On the first Wednesday after his arrival he drove out in his
car to shop in the narrow High Street of the city. On that day,
by the bye-laws, it was the turn for motor-cars to park on the
west side of the street. The Marshal, however, left his car,
unattended, on the east side, while he conducted with considerable gaiety, and even familiarity, a long conversation
with a comely shop-assistant. A big and intractable traffic-jam
resulted. The Marshal emerged at last to find a curious crowd,
two stern policemen, and a long line of vehicles, all hooting

indignantly. When the identity of the delinquent was recognized, however, the scowls of the citizens gave way to smiles. The policeman, in simple terms, explained the bye-law; the Marshal said charmingly, 'I have understand—but I am Freeman—is it not?' and the incident passed off with good-humour.

The next day the Marshal was seen driving very fast along the sea-front, on the wrong side of the road, ignoring the lights, singing a wild old cavalry song, and with a young lady on his knee. When stopped at last and chided by a constable, he said again, with his delightful smile: 'But I am Freeman of Borough —yes?' The officer, with singular tact and intelligence, remarked that the Marshal was a Freeman of Burbleton, but not of Great Britain, and that neither the Corporation nor anyone else could give him licence to violate the general traffic-laws of the kingdom. The Marshal, according to the evidence, took the point at once; and has not since offended in this manner.

The distinction made by the constable, however, may well have fortified the Marshal's evident belief that within the bounds of the Borough he was entitled to ignore the obligations of a citizen of the Borough. There followed, at brief intervals, a series of incidents which have caused disquiet. The first was the great soldier's resolute refusal to pay any rates. A Freeman, he said, must surely enjoy the public services of the Borough— the police, the gas, the water, and so on, free of charge. There seems to be some reason in this contention, and the Corporation at length assented.[1] Similarly, with success, the Marshal declined to make any payment for entry on to the Victory Pier, or for the use of a deck-chair on the Esplanade.

Next came the Rocket Episode. On the fifteenth anniversary of the foundation of the Revolutionary State in his own land the Marshal gathered a number of his compatriots in the evening on the Esplanade. A great many toasts were drunk; a small but active balalaika band played stirring folk-songs, in

---

[1] Before the Municipal Corporations Act, 1935, which respected existing usages, a Freeman was exempt from all 'tolls and dues.'

which the chorus joined, interfering no little with the efforts of the municipal band to please the citizens not far away; and there was a fine display of that acrobatic form of dancing described by one witness as 'dancing sitting down.'

Rockets and other fireworks were then produced and discharged: and finally the Marshal fired one hundred and one live rounds into the air from his revolver in honour of the Revolution. There is, it appears, a very strict bye-law against the use of fireworks on the Esplanade; and one of the rockets discharged at a low angle set fire to the head of the Pier. The fire was quickly extinguished, and for this part of the evening's work the Marshal charmingly expressed regret; but, as to the rest, he again genially reminded the authorities that he was a Freeman.

The Marshal has a large steam yacht which he has berthed in the Harbour, refusing to shift his berth when desired, or to pay any harbour-dues. The Corporation is rightly proud of the various bye-laws and regulations which it has established to keep the practice of sea-bathing within decent and orderly limits. No undressing on the beach, not even 'macintosh-bathing,' is permitted: and all must enter the sea from Corporation huts, within well-defined limits and in standard costumes. The Marshal and his friends have consistently ignored these arrangements. Hilarious parties of young men and women have emerged from his house and noisily entered the sea at all hours of the day and night, in costumes variously described as bizarre, scanty, and Continental, and, on at least one occasion, it is rumoured, in no costumes at all. And the mischief is, say the Corporation, that some of their own citizens are inclining towards indiscipline too.

These assaults upon public order and the decent name of Burbleton at last provoked the Council to firmer action than they had cared to contemplate before. With admirable tact they caused to be conveyed to the Marshal a private intimation that unless he could find it convenient to comply with the local bye-laws, customs and charges his presence in the Borough would be no longer welcome. The Marshal replied laughingly

'But I am Freeman. The people love me.' Which appears to be true.

What are the Corporation to do? They cannot eject him, for he is a freeholder. It would be odious to prosecute the great man whom they have delighted to honour for what many would think to be small offences. Moreover, they are not sure of their position at law: and they have come to this Court for a declaration.

The Court holds, with some reluctance, that they have brought this trouble on themselves. By the way, does the Marshal get a vote?

Mr. Mould (for the Marshal): The rights and privileges of a Freeman, milord, in the old days, generally included the right to vote at a Parliamentary election of the borough. Whether a Freeman of foreign birth——

The Judge: Well, there you are. There must be some substantial significance in the appellation 'Freeman,' or it would not have been made the subject of an Act of Parliament. That significance can only be a degree of freedom within the Borough not enjoyed by the citizen who is not a freeman. Discretion and taste will, no doubt, in most cases suggest the limits within which such a privilege shall be enforced; but, so long as he does not infringe the law of the land, we hold that in Burbleton the Marshal can do what he likes.

4 July, 1945

(10) THE KING *v.* BROADWICK

THE DODGED DEPOSIT

A JUDGMENT which must have a profound political effect, and may even, it is considered, lead to a General Election, was delivered by Mr. Justice Twigg to-day.

These proceedings, said his Lordship, arise from an application by the good Mr. Haddock, whose interventions in the forensic field have caused so much happy and fruitful deliberation.

The nature of the case can be briefly indicated. Mr. Haddock asks that there should be issued to the Returning Officer of Burbleton (West), the prerogative writ of *Quare benevolentiæ causa*, or (in English), 'Why, for goodness' sake——?' to show cause why he did not, according to law, 'deem' Mr. Q. Smith, M.P., to be 'withdrawn' from the Parliamentary election for Burbleton (West) in the circumstances now to be related.

By Section 26 of the Representation of the People Act, 1918, the celebrated measure of reform which has brought us to the pretty pass in which we find ourselves to-day, it is provided that: 'A candidate at a Parliamentary election, or someone on his behalf, shall deposit or cause to be deposited with the Returning Officer during the time appointed for the election the sum of £150 . . . and if he fails to do so he shall be deemed to be withdrawn within the provisions of the Ballot Act 1872. . . .'

Why exactly, his Lordship proceeded, the Legislature thought fit to place this additional obstacle in the path of citizens offering to serve their country in Parliament is not at all clear. The old and useful custom of the 'preamble' has been abandoned. By the preamble, beginning always with the obscure but pleasant 'Whereas,' before a Bill, or even before a Section, the Legislature used to announce to the people—and,

more important, perhaps, to the judges—the general purpose
of the enactments, and so assisted the people—and the judges
—to interpret, later, the particular words in which it endeavoured to express its purpose, and its decrees.

In the present case, wanting a preamble, the Court is
officially unable to say exactly why a candidate for Parliament
must stake £150 before he is permitted to expose himself to
the rude ordeal of universal suffrage. It is true that if the Court
were to peep, unofficially, into the Official Reports of the
speeches in Parliament delivered during the passing of the Act
the Court might possibly determine what was intended and
desired.[1] But this is by no means certain; for a man can read
a great many lively and persuasive speeches in those Reports,
all tending in the same direction, only to find at the end that
the majority voted for a policy opposed to that of the speakers.
For this, among other reasons, the Courts have always declined
to use such aids in interpreting the Statutes, and we have to
rely on the ingenious theories of leading counsel, assisted by
such modest suggestions as the judges may feel themselves
qualified to offer.

This is a democratic age, and the Act in question is without
doubt a democratic Act. As amended by subsequent Acts it
provides that any man or woman of the age of twenty-one
may vote and, with some exceptions, be nominated at a
Parliamentary election. The humblest hind, the poorest
wage-slave, the unemployed, the illiterate, may 'serve'—mark
the word—in that high place if they can persuade a majority
to send them there. All property qualifications have been
swept away: and only at the old-fashioned universities does
the elector have to pass an intelligence test before he is permitted to vote.[2] It is somewhat surprising therefore that any
citizen who offers to 'serve' in this way is required to put down
£150, and highly surprising that the poor candidate should be
confronted at the outset with what may well be regarded

[1] See Note, p. 55.

[2] And this last survival has now been abolished by the Representation of
the People Act, 1948.

as a property qualification or 'means test' under another name.

I should add, by the way, that if the candidate is elected, or if, though not elected, he obtains more than one-eighth of the votes polled, the deposit is restored to him: but if he does not obtain the magic proportion of one-eighth his money is forfeit to the State. In effect, he makes a bet of £150 that he will obtain one-eighth of the votes. One learned counsel, indeed, has suggested plausibly that, the whole thing being in the nature of a gaming transaction, no Court would assist a successful candidate to recover his money if wrongfully withheld by a Returning Officer.

Now, counsel for the Crown has urged with force an explanation of these bizarre provisions which the Court is inclined to accept. In his view the purpose is to deter the frivolous or 'freak' candidate, the man of straw—politically speaking—from crowding the electoral lists, confusing the electors' minds, and adding without good cause to the national expense. He is therefore required, himself, to risk £150 and to lose it if he cannot satisfy the electors that he is a serious aspirant; and in that sentence, says counsel, the accent should be on *himself*, since a risk which does not fall on a man cannot act as a deterrent.

What happened in this case? Mr. Smith, who gave his evidence with engaging frankness, has told us that he did not risk a penny, nor did any friend of his. A certain bank, it appears, advanced the sum of £150, on condition that he paid £10 to the Party to which he belongs. The same was done by the same bank for all the candidates of his Party, who numbered many hundreds. Mr. Smith himself says that he did not even pay the £10, having taken the firm line that he would not pay a penny to anyone for permission to serve his country.

Now, I asked Mr. Smith what were his relations with the bank. Was he interviewed or examined by the bank? Did any representative of the bank visit the constituency and inquire into his personal qualifications and prospects of success? The answer was No. He had no dealings with the bank whatever.

Still more important was his answer to Question 5,081: Did you yourself expect to succeed?

Answer: No. I was astounded. I did not think I had a chance. In fact, I was not too pleased about it, for I am a poor man.

Question 5,082: If you had had to find £150 out of your own pocket would you have stood for Parliament, Mr. Smith?

Answer: Not on your life, my lord.

A candidate who does not expect to succeed, who thinks that he has no chance, who is not even eager to succeed, and would not have thought of standing if he had had to risk his own money—what is this but a freak or frivolous candidate, the very type of candidate whom, if our interpretation of the Section be correct, it was designed to deter and keep away?

Through the operations of the bank and others Mr. Smith was not deterred; and, for all the Court knows, there were many hundreds of candidates in like case. It may well be that in other proceedings, after fuller inquiry, there may be disclosed a criminal conspiracy to evade and defeat the purpose of a Statute. The fact that Mr. Smith, or others, were in the event elected has no relevance, except perhaps as an aggravating circumstance. Counsel has defended the transaction as a kind of insurance by the bank: but insurance transactions must not be against public policy, and to insure the return to Parliament of frivolous candidates in large numbers must be against public policy. The more successful it is, the more repellent to the law.

Into these wider and attractive fields of thought I must not stray farther to-day. It is enough to say that in this case the writ must issue, as desired, to the Returning Officer, Mr. Broadwick. It was his duty to satisfy himself that Mr. Smith, 'or someone on his behalf' (by which words may be intended his agent, but not a bank of which he had never heard), had deposited, at his own peril, £150: and since it appears that Mr. Smith did no such thing the Returning Officer should have deemed him to be withdrawn. He is to attend this Court to show cause why he did not do so. I am told that my decision may ultimately affect the position of many hundreds of

Members of Parliament. I cannot help that. They should observe the law.

3 October, 1945

NOTE: The Returning Officer duly attended. He said that he knew nothing of any bank. The money was handed in by Mr. Smith's agent and he had no reason to suppose there was anything wrong.

The Judge: But you should have made sure. You should have put to him the simple question: 'Do you assure me that if you fail to gain one-eighth of the votes you will yourself be poorer by the sum of £150?' A man is not likely to begin his political career—or end it— by lying to the Returning Officer.

Mr. Broadwick undertook to put that question to all candidates in the future, and the Judge reluctantly discharged him.

If his Lordship had 'peeped into the Official Report' he would have found much to fortify his opinions. See *Hansard*, 22 May, 1917, Vol. 93, Col. 2,141: 'We further propose that a candidate shall make a deposit, which will be returnable to him if he has not less than one-eighth of the votes. That is intended to prevent mere freak candidates' (Sir George Cave, Home Secretary, moving the Second Reading of the Representation of the People Bill). Colonel Sanders said (Col. 2,153): 'Extraordinary people are returned to the House of Commons. I do not know, if I may use a sporting term, whether my right hon. Friend has carefully weighed the odds in this case. You are giving £150 to get £400 a year for five years—that is, £2,150. It is about 100 per cent. It is a good outside price that a good many sporting men might be ready to take, and I think you want to make that Clause rather stronger in order to stop these *speculative candidatures.*' In Committee (15 August, 1917) Sir Frederick Banbury moved to make the deposit £250, 'to prevent large numbers of bogus candidates coming forward' (Vol. 97, Col. 1,253). Mr. A. Williams said: 'It seems to me that if a man can get one voter he is justified in testing the opinions of the constituency, and that no one has the right to call him a freak' (Col. 1,255). Sir George Younger (Col. 1,257) moved to make it one-sixth instead of one-eighth of the votes. Sir George Cave said: 'I think one-eighth is enough. If a freak candidate gets one-eighth of the votes polled he will be a fairly successful freak.' That amendment was withdrawn also (Col. 1,259).

Earlier (Col. 1,251), there is an illuminating passage. The original clause 19 read:

'A candidate at a Parliamentary election . . . shall deposit with the returning officer, during the time appointed for the election, the sum of one hundred and fifty pounds. . . .'

Colonel Sanders moved to insert after 'election' the words 'or some person on his behalf.' He did this to cover cases in which 'a candidate cannot possibly be present at the nomination. For instance, a candidate is sometimes put up while he is on service abroad. . . .'

Sir George Cave: 'I am advised that these words are really not necessary. If the candidate cannot make the deposit anyone can make it on his behalf, and that comes to exactly the same thing. It is better not to insert the words unless they are necessary, *because I do not in the least want to encourage the idea that candidates may be financed by someone else*. It is far better that the actual deposit should be made by the candidate himself wherever it is possible.' After some argument he agreed to accept, instead, the insertion of the words 'or cause to be deposited' and these words were accordingly inserted.

On the Report Stage (26 November, 1917, Vol. 99, Col. 1,749) it was again moved, this time by Mr. Nield, that the words 'or someone on his behalf,' be added, purely on the ground that 'a candidate may not be in England at the time of the election if the election takes place before the conclusion of hostilities.' Sir George Cave again thought the words 'unnecessary,' but this time did not resist, and they passed into the Bill. But it is quite clear that they were inserted only to safeguard 'these men who are serving abroad,' and that the sense of the House was with Sir George—that is, against deposits 'financed' by others.

The evils that may arise from the 'insuring' of candidates against 'loss of deposit' were vividly illustrated at the General Election of 1950, at which 460 candidates forfeited their deposits. *Quaere*—is not this practice also contrary to the clear intention of Parliament?

See Lord Mildew in *Lord Havers* v. *The Imprudential Assurance Society* (1951). 'In this case,' he said, 'it was like insuring the life of a conscientious suicide.'

(11) HADDOCK *v.* OUNDLE; HADDOCK *v.* SMITH; HADDOCK *v.* THE GENERAL PRESS; HADDOCK *v.* BUZZINGS AND THE BILIOUS WEEKLY; HADDOCK *v.* COOPER

THE WHALE CASE

MR. JUSTICE RATCHET, giving judgment to-day in the '*De mortuis*' case, said:

In this unusual series of actions, which for the general convenience have been heard together, the plaintiff, Mr. Albert Haddock, is suing a number of persons and papers for libel. Mr. Haddock, while a passenger in a small sailing-vessel which was proceeding southward along the coast of Labrador, had the misfortune to fall overboard. What is now known as 'fog conditions,' but the Court still prefers to describe simply as fog, prevailed. The crew did what they could, but were unable to pick up the plaintiff. On that coast at that time of the year are many large icebergs, and in the sub-Arctic water no swimmer could be expected to survive for long.

Accordingly, on the return of the vessel to Newfoundland, the captain sorrowfully reported that the plaintiff must be presumed to have perished in the icy sea. The distressing news was telegraphed to London: obituary notices of the plaintiff's life and professional career appeared in many organs of opinion; and there was a fairly well-attended memorial service at St. Luke's, Brunswick Square.

But a few days later news came to this country that the plaintiff was still alive. Besides icebergs, there are numerous whales in those waters: and, according to the plaintiff's story which he has repeated in the box with a wealth of plausible detail, he was, like the prophet Jonah, swallowed by a whale. He contrasted vividly the warm interior of the mammal with

E

the freezing grip of the ocean. He repelled, under cross-examination, the suggestion that the whale, being fitted with a trellis-like or 'gridiron' structure in its mouth for the purpose of catching small fish, is quite incapable of swallowing a man— or perhaps I should now say, adult male personnel. Not all whales, the plaintiff assured the court, are thus constructed,[1] and, if they were, what would become of the story of the prophet Jonah, which has never yet been doubted—except, maybe, by the prophet's wife on his return. We do not know what she said. We do not know what was said by the wife of Sir Isaac Newton when he informed her that after observing the fall of an apple he had solved the riddle of the spheres. We do not know what comment was made by the wife of William Shakespeare when he announced that he proposed to establish the family fortunes by writing a stage-play called *Henry VI*, Part One. Fortunately, the Court is not required to arrive at a finding of fact upon these points: but it is useful to recall that many stories as unlikely as the plaintiff's have been accepted without a murmur for many centuries. He said, by the way, that the whale was a white whale; and he asserted that in those regions more white whales were encountered than black.[2] When asked if that did not make nonsense of *Moby Dick*, that masterpiece of literature, he answered that that was no affair of his.

Next day, the narrative continued, the whale in question was harpooned by the whaling-ship *Terra Nova* and towed into the whaling-station at Hawkes Bay, Labrador. The carcass was at once cut up, and—fortunately, before the boiling process—the plaintiff was extracted, not much the worse.

Whatever may be thought of this story, which received keen attention throughout the world, there is no doubt that the plaintiff is alive, and indeed is present in court. The defendants' counsel, unwilling to accept the episode of the whale,

---

[1] See *Physeter catodon* (sperm whale): 'size gigantic . . . head immense . . . snout enormous' (*Encyclopaedia Britannica*, Vol. 5, p. 171*b*).

[2] See *Independent Member*, by A. P. Herbert (Methuen & Co.), 21*s*. (absurdly cheap), p. 284: 'I asked the Norwegian (manager) if they ever saw a white whale. He said that they catch many white whales.'

have suggested that in fact he was picked up by the fishing schooner *Heart of Grace*, which brought him to Newfoundland: and this contention, right or wrong, has more relevance than may at first appear to the issue joined before the Court. On his return to England the plaintiff took exception to certain expressions in some of his 'obituary notices.' Death comes unexpected to most men still: and insufficient praise is given to those great newspapers which produce so readily the following morning a careful account and assessment of the careers of public men; though the thought that in so many offices the record is being ghoulishly brought up to date each year in readiness for the last event must be disturbing to anyone in the public eye. The ancient motto *De mortuis* still seems to prevail in these accounts. The plaintiff does not claim that any of his 'obituaries' was deliberately offensive, though he was disappointed by them all. They were not even likely to aggravate the grief of his relatives if he had been dead. But they are, he says, of a character to damage him in his profession now that he is, in fact, alive. In particular, he objected to the suggestion that, though a careful observer and recorder, he was lacking in imagination. Two writers, he complains, hinted that he was a seeker after publicity, though in fact he is the shyest man alive and suffers a sharp physical revulsion when he sees his name in the papers. Why such a charge should be pressed or resented in the case of a writer is not clear to the Court; for if his name is not known to many how can many be expected to buy his books? It would be as reasonable to blame a nun for her retiring ways. But to say that a romantic author has no imagination may well be damaging, all must agree: and the same, perhaps, applies to Mr. Oundle's observation that the plaintiff was deficient in a sense of the sublime.

Now, it is established law that a libel suit cannot be entertained which arises out of anything written concerning a dead person. Other remedies must be sought by the aggrieved family where the dead are defamed. The defendants say that in good faith and upon proper information they presumed the plaintiff to be dead; that what they published was published only on that assumption and would not have been published had they known him to be alive; that any reasonable man would have thought him to be dead; that at the time of publication he was constructively dead; that the libel, if any, was a libel, to all intents and purposes, on a dead man, and therefore cannot be a cause of action.

This argument, though it was pressed with much ingenuity and force by Sir Ambrose Wett, the Court is unable to accept. We find that the plaintiff was in fact alive when the words complained of were published; and the fact that he was in the belly of a whale at the time, if that is true, or swimming in the sea off Labrador, cannot deprive him of his rights at law. Indeed there is something to be said for Sir Roger Wheedle's contention that for a journalist comfortably placed in London to vilify the character of a public man who is in the belly of a whale off the coast of Labrador might well be a circumstance to be thrown into the scale in any assessment of damages.

Equally we must reject the somewhat unworthy suggestion of defendants' counsel that the entire affair was a 'publicity stunt'—or, alternatively, a plot to obtain damages from trusting newspapers. We cannot imagine a man so eager to secure mention, or money, from the newspapers that he will voluntarily step into sub-Arctic waters in foggy weather off the coast of Labrador. On the other hand, as we have indicated already, we cannot find it defamatory to say that a writer seeks publicity. The mere publication of a book is a request for public attention. Smith, therefore, and the General Press are dismissed from the action; though, since they have been rather a nuisance, they will pay the plaintiff's costs.

There remain the other defendants, and the other charges. These they have tediously attempted to justify by reference to the plaintiff's works, seeking to show that for this reason or that he is not worthy of regard as a composer of romantic fiction. Fortunately, I am relieved of any duty to go into all that by the defendants themselves, who have made so much of the story of the whale. After a strong attempt, and indeed inclination, to achieve credulity, I find myself unable to accept the story of the whale. But the manner in which the tale was told, and the doubts which I have felt concerning it, have persuaded me that the plaintiff is richly endowed with the qualities necessary for the writing of fiction, romantic or other —with imagination, with the capacity to assemble corroborative detail, and that indefinable power called plausibility. In short, it is clear to me that all the remaining defendants have libelled the plaintiff in his professional capacity, and they must pay damages, between them, of *about* £10,000—or more, if the plaintiff wishes. What is the next case, please?

19 March, 1947

(12) REX *v.* BOPPLE

'AVOID LITIGATION'

(Before Mr. Justice Codd)

THIS extraordinary case came to a sensational end to-day. Throughout the trial the behaviour of the prisoner has astonished all beholders. Slight, white-haired, mild, respectable and even refined of feature, he does not suggest to the student of psychology the type of man who could violently attack, with a hammer, a Minister of the Crown in the public street, or would glory in such a deed if he were driven to it by some unusual circumstance. Yet at no time, as the net of evidence closed round him, has he shown any sense of guilt, of discomfort, or even apprehension. Indeed, it was noticed by many that as the trial drew near its end he became more cheerful, nodding and smiling to acquaintances in the body of the court.

To-day, at the conclusion of counsels' addresses, the judge summed-up to the jury. He said:

Members of the Jury—Andrew Bopple, the little old gentleman in that dock, stands before you charged with felonious homicide, or murder: and it is for you to say whether he be guilty or no. I do not envy you the task. Your eyes behold the face and form of the prisoner; your ears have heard the evidence concerning him: and your minds may find it difficult to reconcile the two. He does not look like a murderer. One would have said that he lacked both the strength and the spirit of the assassin. Yet the evidence which you have heard is clear and copious; and in the ordinary course I should not have thought it necessary to address you for long. You will, you must, most patiently examine and measure the smallest wisp of doubt that seems to blow his way. But you may well find it impossible to resist the conclusion that the prisoner did in fact, on April 16th—mark the date—at about 11.0 p.m., in Parliament Street, attack with a hammer the Right Honourable Mervyn Jarrow, so that he died.

The defence have remarked that there appears to be no motive for this murder by this man (they did not, by the way, assist the Court and jury to discover one by putting him in the box). The prisoner has been a Civil Servant all his life: but it is uncertain whether he has ever worked in the same office as the late Minister for Drains, and for all we know they had never met before the fatal night. It is not essential, as the deceived husband said, to prove a motive where the facts are plain; but it often helps: and though, of course, you will pay no attention to anything I say, I must tell you that I have formed a theory about motive in this case which I think is rather good.

A few months ago the prisoner, being sixty-five years of age, as you have heard, retired, or rather was retired, reluctantly, from the Civil Service. He has a small pension, but has saved nothing, being the father of seven; and he can no longer live as comfortably as he did. His wife is dead, and, being unwilling to thrust himself into the homes of any of his married children, he lives in a single small room in a dismal neighbourhood. He has a tendency to rheumatism, and probably finds travel about the Metropolis difficult, as in these days the elderly do, even if they are not rheumaticky. Travel abroad to sunny climes is almost impossible. As the taxes and the prices rise, his pension dwindles: and not even the statesmen are predicting an early 'turn' of that particular 'tide.' It would not be surprising, then, if like so many elderly people to-day he felt little enjoyment in the autumn of his life and less hope for the winter.

'Still,' you may say, as men of the world 'this is a common tale; and there is nothing in it which should lead such a man to take his own life, much less another's. "Life is sweet—however disgusting," as the poet Haddock remarked long ago;

and it is still the law of the land that for murder a man must suffer the extreme penalty, to be destroyed by hanging.' That is so; but at the present time that law is in suspense. As I enjoined you before, observe the date. The alleged murder was committed on April 16th. On April 14th the House of Commons, by a small majority, had added a new clause to the Criminal Justice Bill, the effect of which, if it becomes law, will be to suspend for five years the imposition of the death penalty for murder. It is not law yet: it may never become law. For the House of Lords, it appears, is likely to reject the clause when it is considered in Committee, and the House of Commons, in that case, may still agree with them, a month or two from now. But meanwhile it has become law, most strangely, in *effect*: for it was announced, after the decision in the Commons, that reprieve and imprisonment 'for life' would become the rule at once. The logical reasoning is not easy to follow, for the Commons House is only one of the two Houses of Parliament, and only three-eighths of its Members declared themselves in favour of the change. Logically, if the Lords rejected the Clause in Committee, the citizens concerned would all at once be placed on the hanging list again: but that is not likely to happen in this humane land.

All this is highly relevant to the task which has been laid upon you. If you find the prisoner guilty, it will be my duty formally to pass sentence of death upon him according to law. But it is as certain as anything can be that that sentence will not be carried out, that he will go to gaol for the rest of his life, but not to the gallows. Never before in the history of this island has a man been able to take the life of another with that certitude in his mind; and in two months, perhaps, it may be impossible again.[1] You may think it a lucky chance for the prisoner that after a lifetime of peaceable behaviour he was impelled to commit his murder (if he did) when he did.

Or you may think that it was something more than chance. The prisoner, it may be, has not many years to live. It is likely that, in many ways, he would live those years more

[1] It was.

comfortably in prison than he would outside. He would be housed, fed, clothed and doctored by the State, with none of the troubles of rent, repairs, rates and taxes, ration-books and coupons and insurance-payments which beset the free man. I have ascertained that he does not smoke or drink, and will not suffer the same deprivations as other men. An old Civil Servant, he will still enjoy the congenial atmosphere of the State. An educated man, he is sure to be placed in charge of the Library, very soon: and, when he is not there, he will probably be comfortably in bed in the hospital. Many a lonely old man might envy him.

Now, however enlightened may be our theories of punishment, it is clearly undesirable that lonely old men should be encouraged to go about murdering people in order to escape the troubles of ordinary life and to enjoy the security and quiet of prison till they die. I shall in a few years retire myself: but no such comfortable refuge awaits me. Our prisons are about to be reformed: and the better they are the better should it be understood that people cannot get into them without good cause. There should be sincerity in crime, as in everything. A spurious murder is abhorrent to British juridical notions. It is a kind of contempt of Court. But perhaps I have said enough. You had better retire.

The jury, after a few minutes' deliberation, found the prisoner 'Not Guilty.' The prisoner scowled angrily.

The Judge: Andrew Bopple, you are a free man. You will go back into the big world. And serve you right.

Bopple: That was a dirty trick, my lord. I thought I had everything in the bag.

The Judge: Tell me, why did you pick on the Minister for Drains?

Bopple: I had nothing against him, my lord. I never saw him. But somehow I never could stand what he said in the papers.

The Judge: You should apologize to his family.

Bopple: I will, my lord. It had to be someone.

The Judge: And, in future, avoid litigation. You never know where you are.

12 May, 1948

NOTE: And see *Tough* v. *Twigg* (1949), 2 A.C., where a habitual criminal, under the Poor Persons' Rules, asked for a writ of *mandamus* to be issued to a judge who had put him on probation instead of sending him to prison again.

(13) HOUSE OF COMMONS (KITCHEN COMMITTEE) *v.* HADDOCK

THE EGG OF EXCHANGE
(Before Mr. Justice Codd)

SIR RONALD RUTT, K.C.,[1] opening the case for the plaintiffs to-day, said:

May it please your Lordship, I appear for the Kitchen Committee of the House of Commons. As defendant, the Court, no doubt, will be glad to see that veteran litigant, Mr. Albert Haddock, who is always welcome, however erroneous. His present appearance arises out of a gathering of dramatists at the House of Commons, some of whom were Members and some, more fortunate, were not. Mr. Haddock had made himself responsible for the cost of the refreshments provided, which, considering the eminence in their profession of many of the guests, could hardly be described as 'lavish.' Nowadays, if two citizens occupy a dwelling-place consisting of two small rooms and a bathroom where some of the appliances work it is described as a 'luxury' flat. But that word, I am satisfied, is not here appropriate.

At the close of the proceedings, when the bill was presented to him, Mr. Haddock drew a cheque for Ten Pounds (£10) on an egg.

The Court: An egg?

Sir Ronald: If your Lordship pleases—an egg.

The Court: A turkey's egg?

Sir Ronald: No, milord, a hen's egg. Milord, it appears that the defendant, no doubt legitimately, had acquired three eggs, and brought them to the dinner at the House of Commons.

The Court: And the Kitchen Committee are insulted? I do not wonder. But is this a libel action?

[1] Son of Sir Ethelred (now Lord Justice) Rutt.

Sir Ronald: No, milord. The eggs, it appears, were intended as a tribute to the distinguished dramatist who presided over the gathering.[1] On two of them those present wrote their 'autographs,' and these two were duly presented to the President. On the third——

The Court: What a party!

Sir Ronald: Your Lordship will realize that the company included a good many bright and imaginative spirits. On the third egg, then, in small but legible characters, the defendant drew a cheque in the ordinary form of words: a stamp was duly attached and cancelled, according to the Stamp Act, and the whole document, if it can be so described, was presented to the Manager, Major Sidwell, in discharge of the debt. The Manager presented the cheque at the bank having charge of the Kitchen Committee's account, and asked that bank (which I will call Bank B) to collect the money in the usual manner from the defendant's bank (which I will call Bank A). The manager of Bank B, however, demurred to handling the cheque at all, and especially to making himself responsible for forwarding it through the usual channels. It would require, he said, the employment of special receptacles and messengers——

The Court: Was the cheque hard-boiled?

Sir Ronald: No, milord, it was a fresh cheque. Indeed, there is some evidence that it was a new-laid cheque.

The Court: What a waste!

Sir Ronald: That, milord, was one of the considerations which affected the minds of my clients. 'No man,' as Lord Mildew said in a recent case, 'can pretend to full cognisance and understanding of all the rules and regulations concerning the feeding of the King's subjects at the present time.' But it would be unlikely, my clients thought, if there were not some Statutory Rule or Order against the use of a fresh egg as a Bill of Exchange.

The Court: Yes, Sir Ronald, but I thought that in these affairs the House of Commons could do what it liked? Surely,

[1] Major Ian Hay Beith.

that was all settled by the singular but satisfactory case of *Rex* v. *Sir R. F. Graham-Campbell and others. Ex parte Herbert* (*1935*) *1 K.B.*

Sir Ronald: That is the best opinion, milord: but the House has never cared to abuse its privileges, or to set an unworthy example to the people. If it were to get about, they thought, that Members of the House of Commons were in the habit of using fresh eggs as cheques, promissory notes, I.O.Us. or— who knows?—for the transfer of shares or securities, an unfavourable impression might be made upon a people still bravely suffering under the reign of Austerity.

The Court: But stop a moment, Sir Ronald. I think, perhaps, I was a little hasty. Let us see what would happen to the egg. It was, I take it, the defendant's property? There is no suggestion that it was a pilfered or unrationed egg?

Sir Ronald: No, milord. Indeed, in these days the relevant eggs might even have been what are described officially as 'surplus eggs,' though they have still, for most of us, a merely notional existence.

The Court: Pretty notional, I agree, Sir Ronald. Very well. The egg, I suppose, passes from your client's bank, through the Bankers' Clearing House, or whatever it is, to the defendant's bank. They read and obey the instructions on the cheque: and, their duty discharged, return the cheque, as usual, to the defendant. If it were a paper-cheque he could use it to light his pipe: if it is an egg-cheque, he can eat, or, I suppose I should say, consume it. I do not really see what objections can be raised by the Ministry of Food to such a transaction.

Sir Ronald: As your Lordship pleases. But there remains the question of the difficulties of transit——

The Court: Why didn't your bank have the cheque hard-boiled?

Sir Ronald: Milord, that was considered by the bank. But it was thought that the stamp would become detached in the process of boiling, and perhaps the writing be extinguished.

The Court: The stamp, Sir Ronald, could surely have been attached again: and there is nothing, I think, to prevent the holder from attaching and cancelling a new stamp, if necessary. As for the writing, if I know anything of Mr. Haddock, he uses one of those queer new pens which write under water.

Sir Ronald: As to that, milord, I am not instructed.

The Court: Extraordinary. Go on, Sir Ronald.

Sir Ronald: My clients, milord, declined to accept the cheque in payment and presented their account again. The defendant——

The Court: The defendant, I suppose, took umbrage? He said that he was not accustomed to having his cheques scorned and rejected—and you could take it or leave it?

Sir Ronald: That was roughly his position, milord. And he has obstinately refused to discharge the debt.

The Court: Sir Ronald, before you proceed any farther you may care to consult with your clients, and with learned counsel on the other side. It is true that your clients are not bound to accept a cheque of any kind. But in practice, without doubt, many of your debts are collected in this way; and, having regard to the general custom and his own position, the defendant is naturally reluctant to get the name of one who passes worthless cheques. Your clients, or rather your clients' bank, are not in fact objecting to payment by cheque, but to payment by this particular cheque: and the defendant may well have expected to hear some stronger objections than those which you have, so far, exposed. There is nothing magical or mystical about a cheque. It is simply a written instruction by one person to a second person to pay money to a third—to which, of course, a rapacious State insists upon the addition of a stamp. It does not matter where it is written, provided the intention is clear. It can be written on a bill of fare, upon a napkin, or, if no other paper be available, the label of a brandy-bottle, and such cheques have, in fact, passed safely through the banking channels and been duly honoured and met. It could, I suppose, be written on an out-house or the side of a balloon, provided that it was brought effectively to the notice of the bank addressed and the necessary stamp was attached before presentation. Between a brandy-bottle, an outhouse and an egg there can clearly be no great distinction of principle. Nor am I much impressed by the practical difficulties to which you have referred. It is the duty of a bank to keep the stream of commerce flowing and navigable, and to destroy, not to create, new obstacles in the fair-way. You tell me, Sir Ronald, that your bank, because of the brittle and breakable quality of the cheque in question, was reluctant to undertake the responsibility of transporting it to the proper quarter, though all that was necessary, after all, was to place the cheque in the hand of a trustworthy boy (or even girl) and hire a motor-cab. On the other hand, it shrank, I understand, from making the simple experiment of boiling the cheque—and boiling it hard. This, Sir Ronald, was not the spirit of those old merchant venturers who made the name of commercial England famous and admired. Of course, if it became a general practice for men of commerce and industry to employ the egg for such purposes, a state of affairs might arise in which Parliament would feel itself compelled to intervene. But it is always a great mistake to treat the individual on the chance that he may become a crowd. And meanwhile, I, at least, have to deal with the law as it stands to-day. Call Mr. Haddock.

Sir Ronald: But, milord——!

The Court: I am well aware that this procedure is unusual, Sir Ronald. So is the case.

Mr Albert Haddock was sworn and said: Yesterday I wrote in ordinary ink upon an egg the same form of words as were on the egg in this case. I boiled the egg for nine minutes, and the writing was as clear as ever.

The Court: You see, Sir Ronald? The Court will adjourn.

16 February, 1949

NOTE: The later history of this cheque is recorded in Mabane on *Bills of Exchange*. The cheque was hard-boiled by Major Sidwell, conveyed to the defendant's bank, Messrs. Grindlay's Bank Limited, and duly honoured. It is now in the Museum of Queer Cheques at that establishment, cheques drawn on napkins, the labels of brandy-bottles, bills of fare, etc., cheques drawn in verse and uncomplimentary language, cheques illustrated with sketches for the better identification of the drawer and drawee, etc. 'They are all my property,' said Mr. Haddock laughingly in a recent interview, 'and should have been returned to me. But my good Bank has impounded them. Never mind. They have my overdraft too.'

(14) *IN RE* EARL OF MUNSEY: STEWER *v.* COBLEY

THE MISSING DAY CASE

MR. JUSTICE PLUSH said: In this difficult case I have to decide the destination of some enviable property. The deceased testator, the revered Lord Munsey, left all his property (excepting Munsey Castle and Park) to his great-nephew George Stewer '*if he has attained the age of 21 before the date of my death*': and, if not, to his own brother the Hon. Thomas Cobley. Cobley was the heir to the title and Stewer, it seems, to the Earl's affection. So far, so good.

George Stewer celebrated his twenty-first birthday in London on Monday, May 2, 1949, with his widowed mother, Amanda Stewer, who impressed me favourably. A cable of congratulation, dated May 1st, was received from the Earl, who, enjoying a voyage round the world, was then on passage from Honolulu to Sydney in the S.S. *Asthma*.

But a few days later there came a cable from the captain of the vessel:

> DEEPLY REGRET REPORT LORD MUNSEY PASSED AWAY
> TUESDAY MAY 3 BURIED AT SEA IN 10 S 176 E[1] LETTER
> FOLLOWS COOPER MASTER S.S. ASTHMA.

The late Earl, it seems, was very fond of port-wine, which, after a certain age, should be avoided near the Equator. Thomas Cobley, of whom the Court thought very little, succeeded to the title and the Castle; and the grief of the Stewers was allayed by the reflection that, just in time, young George had qualified for his inheritance.

But it had been a near thing, so near that interested parties were naturally anxious, or hopeful, about the possibility of error: and, when the *Asthma* arrived at Sydney the Captain

[1] Latitude 10° South, Longitude 176° East.

F

was interviewed by lawyers acting both for the Stewers and Thomas Cobley. At these interviews a complex question emerged which it is now my duty to elucidate if I can.

It was revealed by Captain Cooper that the Earl, by an unhappy chance, had perished very near to what is known by mariners as the Date Line. As a ship goes round the world in a westerly direction she adjusts her clocks to the sun each day, so that the time is 12 noon and lunch is present in the mind when the sun, as the merry sailors say, is 'over the yard-arm' or reasonably near it. ('Lunch follows the sun,' said Lord Mildew in *Hawaii Harbour Board* v. *Pacific Navigation Company* (1901), or, as some poet has it—probably the man Haddock— 'The farther east, the sooner feast!' for the sun comes, or seems to come, from the east.) But, in so doing, the farther the *Asthma* goes from the meridian of Greenwich the more she falls behind Greenwich Time. Can you explain why, Sir Ambrose?

Sir Ambrose Wett, K.C.: Because every day, milord, as she goes west, away from the sun, the sun rises later, and she must put her clocks back to keep pace with it. Otherwise, in New York, say, where the difference is 5 hours, she would go to bed at 3.0 or 4.0 in the morning.

The Judge: They often do, I believe.

Sir Ambrose: And have lunch at 6.0 p.m.

The Judge: I hope you're right, Sir Ambrose. I'm sure you are. So, when the ship is on the other side of the earth and is approaching the meridian of 180° she will be nearly twelve hours 'slow' on Greenwich, and must add nearly twelve hours to find her 'Greenwich Date.'[1] In practice, of course, it would be

---

[1] 'Consider the hypothetical experience of an aeroplane going round the world in latitude 60° at 450 knots, the Sun's speed in longitude in that latitude. If the pilot starts at noon on a Monday, when the Sun is on his meridian, and flies West, the Sun will remain on his meridian. He will thus experience no day at all. Wherever he is it will be noon and people will be thinking about their midday meal. But when he arrives back on his starting point, the people he left there will be thinking about Tuesday's meal. Somewhere during his journey, therefore, Monday has suddenly become Tuesday. That somewhere is the Date Line, on one side of which people are calling the time noon on Monday, and on the other noon on Tuesday.' *Admiralty Navigation Manual*, Vol. II.

tiresome to change the clocks continually, and the ocean is divided into 'zones,' in each of which for general purposes an exact number of hours is added or subtracted.

Now, a ship—let us call her *Pneumonia*—a few miles on the other side of the meridian of 180°, steaming east, is in the opposite condition. All the way from the meridian of Greenwich she has been gaining on Greenwich: and she is now nearly twelve hours *fast* on Greenwich. Is that right, Sir Ambrose?

Sir Ambrose: Yes, milord.

The Judge: So, in that zone, to find the correct day and hour at Greenwich she must *subtract* twelve hours from the time shown by her clocks. How damn confusing the whole thing is!

But let us return to the *Asthma*. Captain Cooper, who gave his testimony with the refreshing simplicity of the sea, told us that she crossed the meridian of 180° at 1345, by Ship's Time, on Sunday, May 1st, having had lunch earlier every day. The moment before crossing, to find his Greenwich Date, he would have to add twelve hours, which would bring him to 0145 on Monday, May 2nd. But, the moment after crossing, he is in a zone (Zone − 12) where the Captain of the *Pneumonia* must subtract twelve hours to find his Greenwich Date. But if the Captain of the *Asthma* subtracts twelve hours from 1345, on Sunday, May 1st, he is back at 0145 on Sunday, May 1st. He will then be a whole day behind Greenwich Time. To avoid this unfortunate situation it is the custom of the sea to drop or miss one day and so catch up with Greenwich: and accordingly, the Captain told us, at midnight at the end of Sunday, May 1, ship's time, he declared the next day to be Tuesday, May 3. And it was so. Almost at the same moment— 'just after the ship's bell,' said the valet—the Earl died: and at eleven on the same day his remains were committed to the deep.

The *Pneumonia*, on the other hand, must make a similar adjustment, or she will be a day *ahead* of Greenwich. She, I am informed, would repeat a day: she would have two Sundays, May 1, or, better perhaps, two Mondays, May 2. In passing, I hope a mere sedentary judge may be permitted to envy the active life of a sea-captain who is able by his lone decree to create or erase a whole day in the lives of his passengers and crew.

It seems that in a sense, unscientific perhaps, the late Earl had the misfortune to leave this world on the missing day. One rather junior advocate did seem to query whether juridically he was dead at all. But the Captain truthfully reported that he died on May 3. The fact is duly recorded in the log, and upon that fact Sir Roger Wheedle claims that Mr. Stewer should succeed.

On the other hand, it was forcibly argued by Sir Ambrose Wett, for Cobley, that in scientific and physical fact Lord Munsey died on Monday, May 2, and was buried at 2300 that night. He was in vain reminded that there is no reference to May 2 in the ship's log, and no evidence that anything happened on that day in the *Asthma*. Sir Roger mildly remarked that it was going rather far to suggest that an English peer had died on a day of which there is no record, and was buried near midnight an hour before he died, according to the Captain. Sir Ambrose said angrily that he was thinking of Greenwich; Sir Roger said that the Earl did not die at Greenwich or anywhere near it; and the Court had to intervene.

Whatever tricks may have been played with the ship's clocks, Sir Ambrose continued, the Earl died at a point in time which could easily be identified and related to the time of George Stewer's majority by reference to the time at Greenwich. He died, according to the evidence, in Zone − 12, at 0000^h, by Ship's Time, on Tuesday, May 3, and therefore the date of his death was Monday, May 2, the same day as George Stewer's birthday. That being so, said Sir Ambrose, Mr. Cobley was entitled to succeed: for George Stewer had not, according to the terms of the will, 'attained the age of twenty-one *before* the date of the testator's death.'

This somewhat unworthy contention raised the question of the meaning of 'date,' about which learned counsel argued for two or three days. Sir Ambrose said that in ordinary parlance 'date' meant a particular, specified, numbered day. Sir Roger maintained that 'date,' among mariners, and especially 'Greenwich Date,' included the hour as well as the day and the month: that by Sir Ambrose's own showing the Earl had died at about 12 noon G.M.T. on May 2, but young Stewer had come of age, in law, at midnight the day before.

At length, I ruled that about the meaning of 'date' Sir Roger was right: but I called for evidence about the time of George Stewer's birth. No hour is mentioned in the birth certificate.

Sir Roger called Amanda Stewer, who gave her evidence quite charmingly, I thought. She said it was 'before lunch' because of the smell of hot boiled bacon, a favourite dish of her husband's. Sir Ambrose called an aged nurse, who had been in attendance on the occasion. She was sure that the time was one o'clock, because, at the dramatic moment, she heard Big Ben strike the hour. (They lived at Westminster.) That looked, at first, as if Sir Ambrose had prevailed: but in cross-examination it emerged that British Summer Time was then in use. Therefore the time of the majority was 1200 G.M.T., the same time precisely as, according to Sir Ambrose, the Earl passed away. Even then Sir Ambrose submitted that, if the time were the same, George Stewer could not have become twenty-one 'before' the Earl died.

I then caused Captain Cooper to be recalled, in the hope of more precise information. The Captain said, very readily, that it took five and a half seconds to sound eight bells, and so, having regard to the evidence of the valet, he would put the time of the Earl's death at six seconds after midnight on the 3rd by Zone, or Ship's Time, and so at six seconds after noon on the 2nd by Greenwich Mean Time—six seconds later, that is, than the birthday hour.

The Court confesses that it is as nearly confused as it has ever been. My difficulty might have been less, perhaps, if the Earl had been a passenger in the S.S. *Pneumonia*, and the Captain had elected to have two Sundays, May 1, for then by some time or other the Earl might have died on the second

Sunday before the birthday on the Monday. But the Court is far from sure: and, fortunately, it is not necessary to decide the point. The Court (it thinks) has learned a great deal, and is filled with wonder at the arrangements of the sea, by which men can fix and relate exactly to a single standard the deeds and movements not only of men and ships but the heavenly bodies in any corner of the earth or sky. And—oh, Sir Ambrose—how moving it must be to any Briton to think that all this world-wide calculation is done by reference to an imaginary line drawn through a suburb of London called Greenwich!

Moved by these thoughts, by the reasoning of learned counsel, and the beauty of Amanda Stewer, the Court declares that, as a matter of law, by Greenwich Mean Time, the Earl of Munsey died at 12^h 00^m 06^s on Monday, May 2, and so George Stewer succeeds under the will by the small but sufficient margin of about six seconds.

But still some practical doubts remain. The Court is loath, for example, to dispute Captain Cooper's log and say that there must, after all, have been a Monday, May 2, in his well-found ship. If I did that I might lay the whole record of his voyage, upon which so much depends, open to question. And with what trepidation would every master of a vessel approach the Date Line in future! Further, I ask myself, what is to be inscribed upon the memorial stone or tablet—perhaps in Westminster Abbey—which salutes the life, and deplores the death, of the late Earl of Munsey? Certainly it cannot say 'DIED MONDAY MAY 2 IN S.S. ASTHMA': for that would be a lie, an affront to the customs and the records of the sea. I therefore declare that, as a matter of fact, the Earl died, as the Captain says, early on Tuesday, May 3, 1949. This makes no difference to George and his delicious mother: but, for all the Court knows, it may cause all sorts of trouble elsewhere. Leave to appeal will eagerly be granted: and the Court looks forward with respect to reading the judgments of their Lordships in the House of Lords.

7 December, 1949

EDITOR'S NOTE

Fractions of a Day

There was no appeal: but there has been some interested comment in legal circles, and some too hasty criticism, on the judgment of Plush J. in the recent case of *In re Earl of Munsey: Stewer* v. *Cobley* (December 7, 1949). The Earl, it will be remembered, left property to George Stewer 'if he has attained the age of twenty-one before the date of my death.' Stewer 'celebrated his twenty-first birthday' in London on Monday, May 2, 1949: the Earl died at sea on the other side of the world, at a few seconds after midnight May 2–3 (Ship's Time), which, reduced to Greenwich Mean Time, was 12^h 0^m 6^s, on May 2. The Court was at great pains to discover the precise moment of George Stewer's birth, which, by a happy chance, was established at 12 noon exactly, and the learned judge declared that George Stewer succeeded under the will 'by the small but sufficient margin of six seconds.'

Surprise has been expressed that the learned judge did not avail himself of the old common law doctrine concerning Fractions of a Day, which would have put the young man's majority much earlier and saved the Court much troublesome work; and it is thought by some that the case cannot have been fully or accurately reported. Sir Roger Wheedle (for Stewer), it is said, did claim that his client 'had come of age, in law, at midnight the day before': but the learned judge, without further argument, it appears, insisted on determining the exact hour of the young man's birth and basing his decision on that. His Lordship was unquestionably right. It is not to be supposed that he was unfamiliar with the doctrine or the precedents. Some of our correspondents, therefore, have suggested that he may have thought it proper, in the special circumstances of the case, to ignore without mention a doctrine which has been pushed to absurd extremes. But, of course, there was ample authority for ignoring the doctrine: and it is a pity that the cases which, without doubt, guided him were not cited in the report.

The main common law rule, though crazy, is clear enough. Halsbury's *Laws of England* (2nd Edition, Vol. XVII. pp. 582–3) asserts:

'Full age is attained at the close of the day preceding the twenty-first anniversary of birth, but in so much as the law does not take cognizance of fractions of a day, a person is *deemed* to have attained the age of twenty-one

years at *the first moment* of the day preceding the twenty-first anniversary of
his birth, and is therefore capable of acting as a person of full age at any
time on that day.'

Sir Roger Wheedle, then (above), must surely have said 'the last
midnight *but one*.' Lord Mildew's famous ejaculation in *Travers* v.
Travers: 'There is too much of this damned deeming,' will be in the
minds of many. As recently as 1918 (*In re Shurey, Savory and Shurey*
(1 Ch. 263)) the ancient doctrine was affirmed, with evident reluctance, by Sargant J. The testator left his residuary estate upon trust
for such of his three sons, C.S. and two others, 'as shall attain the age
of twenty-five years.' The eldest son, C. S., was born on July 22, 1891,
and died on July 21, 1916—namely, on the day preceding the twenty-
fifth anniversary of the day of his birth. It was *held* that C. S. had
attained the age of twenty-five years at the time of his death. Sargant
J. said that 'the anomaly' began with an Anonymous Case of some
antiquity. 'If one were actually to look at the clock for the purpose
of determining the age of the deceased in that case, it would appear
that he was *one day and twenty-two hours* short of attaining the age of
twenty-one years: but the law does not take cognizance of part of a
day, and the consequence is that a person attains the age of twenty-
one years, or of twenty-five years, or any specified age, on the day
preceding the anniversay of his twenty-first or twenty-fifth birthday,
or other birthday, as the case may be.'

Mr. Justice Sargant used the expression 'anomaly.' Those less
highly placed may prefer the word 'nonsense.' There is something to
be said for disregarding a fraction of a day in many fields of life. An
Act of Parliament, for example, becomes law, sensibly enough, at the
first moment (0000 hours) of the day on which it is passed (an interesting exception was the King's Abdication Act, which, by express
provision and for obvious reasons, became law at the midnight
(2400 hours) after the Royal Assent). And where a man is born at,
say, 11.0 a.m. on May 1, it is sensible enough, in general, to disregard
the eleven hours and say that he becomes twenty-one at midnight
(0000 hours) May 1. But then the law goes mad and disregards 'as
a fraction' the *whole* of the *preceding* day.

The twisted logic of this affair, we understand, runs as follows:

'The Law disregards part of a day: *de minimis non curat lex*. A child
must therefore be regarded as born at the *first* moment of its natal
day: so it completes the first year of its life at the *last* moment of the
day before the "first birthday." But, again *the Law disregards part of*

a day: so a child completes the first year of its life at the first moment of the day before its "first birthday." It therefore completes the first twenty-one years of its life, and comes of age, at the *first* moment of the day before its twenty-first birthday.'

The fallacy, as a learned reader points out, lies in regarding the period between the first and last moments of a day as a *part* of a day. The law should surely correspond to the facts and customs of life, and say that a man comes of age on his twenty-first birthday—meaning the twenty-first anniversary of his birth.

That this is the commonsense view is shown by Section 79 of the National Health Insurance Act, 1911[1] in which our wise Parliament prescribed as follows:

'A person shall be deemed (for the purposes of Part I of the Act) according to the law in England, Wales, and Ireland, as well as according to the law in Scotland, not to have attained the age of seventeen until *the commencement of the seventeenth anniversary of the day of his birth*, and similarly with respect to other ages.'

This section was referred to by counsel in the Shurey case as an indication that the common law was as we have stated it: for otherwise the section would not have been necessary.

Presumably, then (but *quaere*), a man born on Jan. 3 could become twenty-one at midnight Jan. 1–2 for general purposes, but not till midnight Jan. 2–3 for the purposes of the Act.

A correspondent with a morbid turn of mind puts the problem of 'twins, one of which is heir to an earldom. It is an established fact that A was born an hour before B on May 2. But the doctrine of Disregarding Fractions must surely mean that for the purposes of inheritance they were born simultaneously two midnights earlier, at 0000 hours on May 1?'

Another correspondent suggests that the common law doctrine of Disregarding Fractions is inconsistently applied to births and deaths. In *Lester* v. *Garland* (1808), 15 Vos. at 257 (English Reports Vol. 33), a testator bequeathed the residue of his estate to X on condition (*inter alia*) that X gave to the trustees of the will such security as they might approve within six calendar months from his decease. The Testator died on January 12, 1805, and the security was given on July 12, 1805.

Held per Sir William Grant, M.R., that the six months began to run at the commencement of the day *after* the testator's death.

[1] Re-enacted in the National Health Insurance Act, 1946.

In other words, in this case the law, still disregarding fractions, worked forward instead of backward. If Plush J., therefore, had followed the precedents on both sides he would have had to find:

(*a*) that George Stewer attained his majority thirty-six hours *before* the twenty-first anniversay of his birth: and

(*b*) that the Earl was alive throughout Monday, May 2, and did not die legally till twelve hours (less six seconds) *after* his actual death.

Fortunately, there is a good answer to such conundrums. It was laid down long ago by Lord Mansfield in *Combe* v. *Pitt* (1763), 3 Burr. 1423, that 'Though the law does not, in general, allow of the fraction of a day, yet it admits it in cases where it is necessary to distinguish.' So 'Where the defendant died between eleven and twelve in the morning and a writ of *fieri facias* was sued out against him between two and three in the afternoon of the same day, the Court will set aside the writ as irregular. *When it is necessary to show which was the first of two acts*, the Court is at liberty to consider fractions of a day.' (*Chick* v. *Smith* (1840) 8 Dowl. 337).

In a later case (*Campbell* v. *Strangeways*, 3 C.P.D. 105) Grove J. said: '*Chick* v. *Smith* and other cases explain where the law will distinguish the fractions of a day, viz. *where it is necessary* . . . for the purpose of a decision *to show which of two events first happened*.' *Clarke* v. *Bradlaugh* (1881), 8 Q.B.D. 63 (Court of Appeal), is a decision to the same effect.

These authorities clearly cover the misleading case of *In re Munsey*, and, though not mentioned in the report, were, without doubt, in the mind of Plush J. Enough has been said, at least, to show that much of the adverse comment on his judgment was hasty and ill-informed. Good, however, may result. It is to be hoped that Parliament may now come to the rescue of the courts, abolish the monster they have created, and make the rule provided by the National Health Insurance Act general, retaining of course the special exceptions required by such cases as *Chick* v. *Smith* and *In re Munsey*—and applying the same rule to death.

If not, the old doctrine may well be extended to other fields. If the law indeed 'disregards fractions of a day' a publican may have a good answer to a prosecution for selling liquor half an hour after the end of 'permitted hours.' The *Laws of Cricket* may require attention. A batsman who is out at ninety-nine should surely be 'deemed' to have scored 100. *De minimis non curat lex*.

The exhibit below may perhaps make the problem clearer to the practitioner and student.

X. is born at 11.0 a.m. on 1 May 1900
He dies at 11.0 a.m. on 1 May 1950

Becomes 21 at Common Law	0000 hours April, 30 1921	Halsbury
Becomes 21 by National Health Insurance Act	0000 hours May 1, 1921	
Dies—at Common Law	2400 hours May 1, 1950	*Lester* v. *Garland*
Comes of age— by proposed law	0000 hours May 1, 1921	Unless necessary to decide priority between two events. (Lord Mansfield)
Dies—by proposed law	0000 hours May 1, 1950	

(15) MORTIMER *v.* THE BRITISH BROADCAST-ING CORPORATION AND OTHERS

SUNDAY ON THE AIR

AT Bow Street to-day the Chief Metropolitan Magistrate announced his decision in this important case. Mr. Mortimer, a common informer, laid an information against the B.B.C. and some of their servants for an offence against the Sunday Observance Act 1677. The Attorney-General appeared for the defendants.

Though I took time to consider my decision, said the magistrate, the case seems clear enough. On Sunday, May 21, between 9.15 and 10.45 p.m. the defendants caused to be performed on their premises at Alexandra Palace 'a comedy by Arnold Bennett' called *The Title*: and by a process called television the performance was made visible and audible in the homes of the many thousand subscribers or licensees. The laws concerning private labour and public entertainment on the Lord's Day are in this country severe; and, in particular, the presentation of stage-plays at a play-house has been prohibited, under heavy penalties, since the reign of George III (Sunday Observance Act, 1781). 'If a house, room or place be opened for any public entertainment, or for debating upon any subject, on Sunday, to which persons are admitted only by payment, the keepers thereof shall forfeit £200, the manager or president £100, the receiver of money or tickets £50, and every person printing an advertisement of such meeting £50.' Even when by Act of Parliament, in 1932, the exhibition of moving-pictures, for money, on Sundays, was made lawful, performances by living actors were carefully excluded.

So far as it is possible, or proper, to interpret the mind of the Legislature, it seems to consider the actor in two ways:

(1) as a person whose lewd and worldly performances should not be allowed to corrupt and distract the citizens from religious contemplation on the evening of the Lord's Day, and (2) as a worthy and God-fearing person who should not be compelled, or even permitted, to labour on the Lord's Day for the selfish enjoyment of others. Whether the main purpose was the protection of the citizen or the protection of the actor, it has not prevented actors from using their gifts and experience on Sundays in the service of the B.B.C. and in programmes which it would often be difficult to describe as unworldly. The invention of television took the thing a long way farther, for now the actors are using all the apparatus of a stage-play. They paint their faces, they wear costumes, are surrounded by scenery and artfully illuminated. Mr. Mortimer —a deeply religious man, he assured the Court—is persuaded that such performances are contrary to the intentions of the authors of the Act of George III, and, in a sense, are more harmful than the production of a stage-play in a play-house. Few, he says, but the lewd and worldly might be attracted to such a place on a Sunday: but by television the unwholesome influences of the theatre are brought into the homes of the people and assail the young and innocent by their own hearths, even, it may be, at their mothers' knees.

His difficulty lies in the wording of the Act. Though it is evident that the defendants are providing a 'public entertainment' no one is admitted to any house or place 'only by payment' in order to enjoy it. If he had relied upon the Act of George III, I should have been compelled to dismiss the case at once.

But he has drawn the Court's attention to the wording of the Act of Charles II, which provides that:

'No tradesmen, artificers, workmen, labourers, or other persons whatsoever shall do or exercise any worldly labour, business, or work of their ordinary callings upon the Lord's Day, or any part thereof (works of necessity and charity only excepted).'

There are, in fact, other exceptions. Barbers are excluded:

and farmers, attorneys, and surgeons do not come within the classes mentioned in the statute. It would be an abuse of language, perhaps, to describe an actor as a tradesman, workman or labourer. But many of those who attend and are necessary to his performance fall clearly into one or other of those categories; the man, for example, who places the scenery and the arc-lights, the carpenter, the property-man, the man who acts as his dresser or guards the door of the building. Then there are the 'artificers.' These are defined in *Wharton's Law Lexicon* as 'persons who are masters of their art and whose employment consists chiefly in manual labour.' Here, I have no doubt, should be included all the higher grades of theatrical labour of this kind: the electrician who regulates the flow of light, the man who directs the camera or the sound-recording, the lady who assists the actress in her make-up, adjusts her wig and fits her dresses.

The *Oxford English Dictionary*, I need hardly say, gives six different meanings, three of which I think are richly relevant to our purpose: (1) 'One who makes by art or skill,' (4) 'Contriver, inventor, deviser' and (5) 'One who practises any art, or applied science.' These, between them, seem to me to cover almost all those who contribute actively to a theatrical production on the Lord's Day. The producer and stage-manager are, without doubt, contrivers and devisers, 'making' something by their art and skill. No actor would be heard to say that he is not 'one who practises an art': indeed, that is the whole of his somewhat flimsy claim to consideration. Only the author, I think, escapes. It must be assumed, in the absence of evidence to the contrary, that he is a God-fearing man and wrote his play on a week-day: and, unless he actively assists at a Sunday rehearsal, he should be blameless. All the other individuals concerned in this performance I find guilty of an offence, and they will forfeit five shillings.

There remains the question of the principal defendants, the British Broadcasting Corporation. I should be reluctant, indeed, to punish the small man under orders and let the responsible employer go free. Such injustices cannot always be avoided: but here I am in no doubt. The Corporation is clearly an 'artificer' within the meaning of the Act. If the defendants think themselves too high and mighty for such a title, I can but remind them that the Creator has been described as the Artificer of the Universe. The Corporation will pay five shillings too. I am aware that this decision, though concerned with television and stage-plays only, must raise some anxious doubts about the legality of all the Corporation's activities on Sunday. I cannot help that: but I should be willing to state a case for the opinion of a higher Court.

14 June, 1950

NOTE: And see a sparkling speech in the House of Commons, April 1, 1941: 'Let us look at what happened last Sunday. According to the *Radio Times*, there were no fewer than seven theatrical entertainments put forward by the B.B.C. last Sunday.

'The entertainments, which were performed by professional actors, would be unlawful in the theatre outside. At 4.30 in the Home Service programme, at the time when in Victorian days the children were massing about their mothers' knees, there was a performance, with elaborate music and dialogue, of the degrading stage play called *Peter Pan*. It lasted one and a quarter hours. At 9.25 there was a play by the alien writer Euripides. The position was far more serious on the Forces programme, where there were at least five such performances. At 12.30 there was "Services Variety," at 1.15 "Music Hall," and at 2.15 "Sunday Matinée," and at 6.30 something called "Hi-Gang." All these performances were given by well-known actors and actresses. At 8 o'clock an entertainment with the horrible name of "Happidrome" was given, and at 10.8 there was Bobbie Pagan at the theatre organ.

'Meanwhile, as my hon. Friend has already pointed out, on Sunday in Fleet Street and in every other big town there were hundreds of thousands of men preparing Monday's *Times* and *Express* and all the papers which my hon. Friend reads in bed on a Monday without a protest or a qualm. Let me put it in another way. Take it from the point of view of a well-known actor, like John Gielgud. On Sunday, if the B.B.C. like, he can act *Hamlet* or *Henry V* all day long. He can appear on the films as Hamlet or Henry V. He can give a long lecture on *Hamlet* or *Henry* V. He can appear—this is remarkable—at a concert or cinema and act passages from *Henry V* so long as he does not make up, put on costume, and do the job properly. In other words, I think we are trying to keep the horse in the stable long after it is far away.' (*Petty Officer Alan Herbert, Oxford University.*)

(16) CANTER AND OTHERS *v.* HOWARD

THE CANTER POLL

(*Before the Lord Chief Justice*)

HIS Lordship, giving judgment, said: In this important case a writ of *habeas corpus* was issued to the defendant Howard on behalf of three persons, Dr. Canter, Mr. Knocknee and Miss Gambier-Truce, who were said to be held in custody without due cause or legal process. This great prerogative writ is one of the finest props, foundation-stones, keystones, bulwarks, sheet-anchors and so forth of liberty in this fair land: and black will be the day when it loses power or respect. But in this case the defendant Howard is none other than Sir Charles Howard, Serjeant-at-Arms to the House of Commons, and it was in obedience to an Order of that honourable House that he confined the three complainants in the Clock Tower at Westminster.

Now, it is well established that either House of Parliament can do almost anything it will (short, perhaps, of execution) to any person who offends it. Certainly, it can, for breaches of privilege or contempt, commit any person to custody: and, in general, the causes of the commitment cannot be inquired into by any court of law, though it is the practice for the Serjeant-at-Arms to make a return to a writ of *habeas corpus*. There is, however, one exception to this healthy doctrine. When the warrant for arrest or commitment goes beyond the general assertion of contempt and breach of privilege and states particular causes for the infringement of liberty complained of, the Court (*per* Lord Ellenborough in *Burdett* v. *Abbot*) may inquire whether the causes disclosed are sufficient and within the jurisdiction of the House. In this case particular causes were set out in the warrant: and this Court gaily accepts the

challenge—or, it may be, the invitation—of the High Court
of Parliament.

The charge is that Dr. Canter and his friends 'did falsely
purport to take a poll of the people in relation to the constitution of Parliament and did publish the same contrary to
the Representation of the People Acts and in derogation of
the rights and dignities of the Commons House of Parliament.'

The complainants frankly confess that they are responsible
for an institution called the Canter Poll which from time to
time announces that the popularity of the Prime Minister has
risen from 51·3 to 52·6 per cent., while the chances of his Party
at the next Election have fallen from 37·5 to 33·8 per cent.

The 'poll' is an essential part of British democratic practice,
whether the scene be great or small. There may be a poll of
a parish, a city, a county, a private society, a limited liability
company, a House of Parliament, the nation. But what is a
'poll'? Literally a poll is a 'head.' Socially, and politically, it
means a counting of heads, whether at a census, an election,
or similar occasion. It is an exact and mathematical process,
opposed, for example, to such uncertain guides to opinion as
the 'show of hands.' This distinction is familiar to the Courts;
for, whenever a person has to be chosen, or a thing may be
ordered to be done, by a majority of the persons entitled to
vote, there is a Common Law right to demand a *poll*, so that
all entitled to vote may have a second and fairer opportunity
of voting (*Reg.* v. *Wimbledon Local Board* (1881), 8 Q.B.D.—
459—C.A.). And, whatever the scene or scale of affairs, the
meaning of 'poll' is plain enough to the ordinary citizen of
'reasonable' intelligence.

But in this affair, it is clear, the word has no such meaning.
There are about fifty million inhabitants of the United
Kingdom, and about thirty-four million Parliamentary voters.
Dr. Canter admitted in the box that the questions upon which
his 'poll' is founded are addressed to about two thousand only.
There is no secret, it appears, about the figure two thousand:
but it is not published with the 'results' of the 'poll,' and so,
for any misunderstanding that may arise, the promoters must

be held responsible. The announcement of a "poll-tax" which was to be levied upon one in every twenty-five thousand citizens would be greeted with public derision: and no more respect, it is clear, is due to the 'poll' in 'Canter Poll.' Whatever it is the Doctor does, he does not count *all* the heads.

So much, under cross-examination, he conceded. But he said that his two thousand were a 'cross-section' of the people, so cleverly, so 'scientifically,' selected, that their opinions 'represented a poll.' A contradiction in terms: but let that pass, for the moment. Further, he claimed with pride that upon certain important occasions the predictions, or premonitions, founded upon his 'Poll' had been confirmed, or nearly confirmed, by events, that is, by the voting of the people at a subsequent election. I must say at once that all this boasting did not impress the Court. Not only the method, but the matter must be considered. It may be innocent, and useful, to ask one in every twenty-five thousand of the people how often they wash, what they think about the South Bank, or whether, when cleaning brass or silver, they use Bozo or Shinit, and to found upon their answers certain general conclusions. But when the questions are: 'Do you like the Prime Minister?' or 'How will you vote at the next Election?' (which is as much as to say 'Do you think the House of Commons is properly constituted at the present time?') we must halt for reflection. Here, it seems to me, the more right the complainants claim to have been in fact, the more wrong they are in law.

'Two rights,' as Lord Mildew said in a famous case,[1] 'may well make a wrong.' For our ancient Constitution has provided means by which these questions can be put and answered; and Dr. Canter, so far as this Court is aware, has no place in the Constitution. Speaking as a citizen, and not as a Judge, I feel an inexpressible repugnance when I read that the Prime Minister has declined in popularity from 48·9 to 47·3

[1] *The Queen* v. *Merino* (*1901*), A.C.1, where a crystal-gazer told two clients, both married, that they would meet a dark woman and a tall fair man respectively. They did: and, according to the newspaper-report, 'became involved in a suicide pact.'

per cent., however little I may agree with him politically. What an impertinence! Speaking as a Judge, I am sure that it is against public policy and constitutionally improper. Any statesman, it is true, any journalist, is free to say that in his opinion the Prime Minister, or the Party in power, have lost the confidence of the country, and should 'go to' it. It is quite another thing to pretend that by 'scientific' means you have discovered the opinion of thirty-four million people. For this must be untrue, and if it were true, would make elections unnecessary and the Constitution nonsense.

So far, then, as this Court has any say in the matter, I find that the complainants were incarcerated for good cause: and they will return to their noisy quarters in the Clock Tower. In time, no doubt, the House of Commons will mercifully discharge them. The question will then arise whether they should be dealt with as rogues and vagabonds, pretending to tell fortunes 'by palmistry or otherwise,' or as the authors of seditious libels 'tending to bring into hatred and contempt' the Constitution as by law established, and the House of Commons, in particular. Upon that, at the moment, I express no opinion.

6 June, 1951

(17) REX v. HADDOCK AND VINE

BOOKMAKERS ALL

'ONE of the most shameless frauds on the Revenue ever conceived,' said the Attorney-General, Sir Anthony Slatt, in his final address to the jury at the Old Bailey to-day. 'You will know what to do,' he concluded grimly.

Mr. Justice Codd, summing-up to the jury, said:

The learned Attorney-General has allowed himself to become more excited than is customary in counsel prosecuting for the Crown. That, in the circumstances of this case, is understandable: but you must not allow his emotion to affect you. Nor should you be swayed by the almost universal loathing for the prisoner Haddock. Address your minds to the facts, and to so much of the law as I am able to explain.

No excitement was caused, a year or two ago, when the ancient and respected firm of Lotwood put the words 'Bookmakers and' before the word 'Publishers' on their fine building and elegant notepaper. After all, it is part of their business, as the Memorandum of Association says, to 'prepare, devise, make and manufacture' books: and the addition was thought, by the few who noticed it, to be an unnecessary but pardonable essay in precision.

But one of Lotwood's authors is the notorious Albert Haddock who stands before you in that dock to-day. This man is chiefly known for his unreasoning and unrelenting objection to the rates of income tax and the methods of the selfless officers whose duty it is to assess and collect it. But again, members of the jury, though, as good citizens yourselves, you may delight and glory in the income tax, I must adjure you to put aside such odious sentiments as may naturally arise in you towards weak, eccentric characters who do not think as you do.

In February this year the officers of the Inland Revenue Department were placidly planning, according to law, to take away from Albert Haddock two-thirds or more of the money he had earned by his brains and labour in the two preceding years. During their kindly researches into his banking account —which, to do the prisoner full justice, was offered for their inspection—they came upon a 'credit' entry of £1,000, a cheque signed for that amount by Mr. Stanley Vine, the general manager of Lotwoods. 'This,' they said, 'is, we presume, part of your professional earnings, an "advance on royalties" for one of your books, perhaps?' 'No, no,' said the prisoner; 'that was my winnings on a successful bet—and, therefore, is not subject to income tax.' 'What was the bet?' said the officer. 'That,' said the prisoner, 'has nothing to do with you. I do a good deal of betting with Mr. Vine,' he added, and he indicated in the bank-book several small payments to Mr. Vine. These, he said, were for unsuccessful bets on horses and dogs. You snorted at that, didn't you, Sir Anthony?

The Attorney-General: Milord?

The Judge: Never mind. The Inland Revenue then visited the Lotwood office, where the prisoner Vine, it appears, was as frank and open as he has been in the box. The Memorandum of Association says that the company may conduct 'any other business whatsoever which can be advantageously carried on by the company': and side by side with the ordinary business of producing and marketing books in the literary sense his firm are now conducting the business of a credit 'bookmaker,' in the sporting sense. So far as the Court knows, there is no objection to this in law. Many citizens, including the prisoner Haddock, and at least two Royal Commissions, have recommended that all 'bookmakers' should be registered and licensed. But the Legislature has never thought fit to provide for this. Indeed, in these days, it is about the only thing that can be done without a licence. Anyone, therefore, can set himself up as a bookmaker, if he so desire, and, provided he sticks to credit-betting, and does not allow persons to resort to his office for the purpose of betting, nobody can interfere with him. Of course, he will have to produce his accounts to the Inland Revenue and pay tax upon his profits, if any.

Further, as counsel for the defence have suggested, you may think that there is a special affinity between these two types of business. As the prisoner Vine told the Court, 'Nothing could be more like a gamble than the production and sale of works of art.' Some of Vine's bets, it seems, have been directly connected with the other branch of the business. Authors, he told us, are sometimes idle, sometimes temperamental, always uncertain. He may sign with them a generous contract for the production of a novel in time for the spring season, with an advance on royalties to be paid on delivery of the manuscript. Paper is bought: the printers stand ready. Years pass; no novel appears: and there is nothing he can do about it. But such febrile characters, he says (and, after all, he should know the psychology of his business best), are often stimulated by the challenge of a bet. Accordingly, sometimes, he will bet Author A £500 that he will *not* deliver his new book by April 30. Author A, as a rule, he says, roars into action, toils day and night, produces the book on time, and wins the bet— to the advantage of all concerned.

The £1,000 payment to the prisoner Haddock, it was revealed in evidence, was the result of what you may think to have been a singularly 'sporting' wager. Haddock bet Vine £1,000 that his book *Forty Years of Fun* would sell five thousand copies. In fact, it sold many more than that. Vine paid up like a man, and the payment, of course, being a betting payment, was free of income tax.

It does not appear that the bookmaking side of Lotwood's business is very successful. The cheques paid out by Vine are generally large: the bets he wins are often small. But that may happen to anyone in the gambling business. At the end of the last financial year the business showed a loss: but that loss of course he is entitled to set off against the profits of the publishing business as any man who runs two businesses may do. Vine, it is said, hopes for better things in the current year, and, meanwhile, is borrowing money from the publishing side, with whom he is on good terms.

So far, you may think, the story does not disclose anything that calls for the attention of a criminal court. The Crown, however, say that here is a criminal conspiracy between Vine and Haddock, and Vine and other authors, to avoid payment of income tax. Let it be said, at once, that the avoidance of tax is not necessarily an offence or even wrong. The prisoner Haddock could avoid tax by ceasing to write at all: and so harsh is the treatment of authors that it would not be surprising if he did. But it would be no crime. And, if a man chooses to acquire money by betting (untaxed) rather than by hard work (taxed), that, again, is his own affair. Haddock, in the box, shyly admitted that, elated by winning a bet of £1,000 from Mr. Vine, he waived his royalties on the first five thousand copies of *Forty Years of Fun*. The Attorney-General found something fishy in that. You may think, as the Court thinks, that it was a very generous gesture. At all events, Mr. Haddock is not bound to accept the royalties due to him. If he chooses, he can write for fun and give his books away.

The Attorney-General: But, milord——

The Judge: I know, I know, Sir Anthony. To the Treasury, of course, any transaction that does not yield them a fat harvest is tainted: but that is not the law.

The Attorney-General painted a lurid picture of what may happen if the prisoners are acquitted. All sorts of firms, he said, film companies, theatrical managers, banks, will set up ancillary bookmakers' businesses and millions of pounds will go free of tax as winning bets. That may be. But it does not mean that the transactions we are considering are illegal. It may mean that the law requires amendment. That is the business of Parliament. It is our business—yours and mine—to administer the law as it stands. Consider your verdict.

The jury found the prisoners *Not Guilty*, and recommended a complimentary grant to them from the public funds.

13 June, 1951

NOTE: See also *Board of Inland Revenue* v. *the Dean of Alnwich* (1952), H.L., where the defendant made a successful wager of £5,000 with the Ecclesiastical Commissioners that a certain number of persons would attend divine service at the Cathedral within a certain period. *Held* (Lord Moon dissenting) that the payment was not liable to tax, though it was proved that the defendant had waived certain emoluments.

(18) THOMAS v. LOWDER; LOWDER v. THOMAS

THE LAW OF THE BAR

M R. JUSTICE PLUSH, giving judgment, said: These two actions, which for convenience have been heard together, concern an incident which is happily rare in the life of our land, the forcible ejection of a police-officer from a public house. Mr. Thomas is a constable, a good officer, according to his superiors, but young and inexperienced. Mr. Lowder is the licensee of the Blue Moon at Burbleton.

'Permitted hours' in the Borough of Burbleton end at 10.30 p.m. At 10.42 p.m. (B.S.T.) on the night in question Constable Thomas heard voices 'proceeding,' as he put it, from the saloon bar. He opened the door and entered, as any constable may do, without warning or warrant, if he has reasonable cause to suspect a breach of the law. There had been, that evening, a skittles match between the Blue Moon Club and the Lord Nelson Club (of Lower Wallop) and in the bar, besides the landlord, were about a dozen men discussing the affairs of the skittle world in general and the victory of the Blue Moon that evening in particular.[1] Is it 'skittles' or 'skittle,' Sir Eliot?

Sir Eliot Ember, K.C.: They speak milord, of playing 'skittles.' But the governing body is called the Amateur Skittle Association.

The Judge: Very singular. Ha! But the evidence is clear that at 10.30 all drinking had stopped and that none of the men had even glasses in their hands. Mr. Lowder, it appears (a teetotaller, by the way), is almost pedantic in his observance of the law. At 10.20 he rings an old ship's bell and cries,

---

[1] In the 1950–1 season members of the Blue Moon Skittles Club (President, Mr. Albert Haddock) won eight out of the sixteen trophies presented by the Amateur Skittle Association.

'Last orders, please.' At 10.25 he rings the bell twice and calls 'Finish your refreshments, please.' At 10.29 the bell is rung for the last time and all glasses are collected or handed over the bar. This precise ritual had been observed that evening.

But Constable Thomas, standing at the door, said suspiciously, and, according to one witness, offensively, '*Rather late, aren't you?*'

'Late?' said the wounded licensee, indignantly. 'What's it got to do with you? There's no one drinking. Have a look.'

The constable 'had a look.'

'Satisfied?' said Mr. Lowder.

'Yes,' said the officer.

'Good,' said the licensed victualler. 'And now get out. I've private business with my friends here.'

'Don't talk to me like that,' said the officer. 'I'm doing my duty.'

'You've done your duty,' said Mr. Lowder. 'Out you go, please. What's more, I'll be glad if you withdraw the remark you passed. This is a respectable house.'

'Remark? What remark?' said the officer.

'About being late. It's no business of yours what time we go to bed.'

'I meant you were late shutting up.'

'That ain't your business, either,' was the reply. 'If you don't apologize, you go.'

'I'll go when I'm ready,' said the officer: and he added, unworthily: 'How do I know you won't start boozing when I've gone?'

'Because I tell you,' said the indignant victualler. 'I'm a liar now, am I? Here, out you go!'

With these words, he put a hand on the officer's shoulder and quietly but firmly conducted him out, to the astonishment and awe of his companions. The constable brought an action for assault, and Mr. Lowder issued a writ for slander.

It is now necessary to explore the legal significance of this spirited and unusual encounter. Loathsome though the provisions of the Licensing Act, 1921, must appear to any thinking citizen, that measure had one point of merit. It abolished what was known as 'closing-time.' The sale and consumption of 'alcohol,' as it is called, can only take place within certain 'permitted hours': but the inn need never be 'closed.' It is lawful to enter or stay upon licensed premises at any hour of the day or night, if the landlord is agreeable. A man could sit in the public bar all day, playing backgammon, or chess, without breaking the law, though, if the landlord desired him to go and he refused, he would become a trespasser.[1] The landlord, on the other hand, can converse with friends in the public bar all day, if he will, as freely as in his private parlour. This beneficent distinction should be more widely known than it is: and I hope that it will be impressed upon all young policemen. For it does something to correct, on the one hand, the notion that the inn or public house is a place for 'boozing' only, and, on the other, the sense of regimentation which must come from punctual expulsion at fixed hours. It is a pity, perhaps, that so many licensees bring back the atmosphere of 'closing-time' by churlishly bustling their customers out as soon as 'permitted hours' are over: but they are under no obligation, one way or the other.

Now, as has been said, Constable Thomas, if he had reasonable cause to suspect that an offence was being committed, had a right, a duty, to enter the bar. Having satisfied himself, as he admitted, that there was no offence, his duty was to depart at a reasonable pace: for, in the absence of an invitation from the landlord, he was intruding on a private gathering. He had no right to remain there on the vague suspicion that an offence *might* be committed in the future: for, if he could do that, he could sit in the bar all day; and Parliament has expressly provided against such behaviour. When he was requested to go and refused, he became a trespasser: and as a contumacious trespasser Mr. Lowder was entitled to use

[1] See *Rex* v. *Lambert* (1945) where 'for a record' a man sat 12 hours in the public bar of the *Black Lion* drinking soda-water, as a result of which he swelled up and died. It was *held* that no offence against the Licensing Laws had been disclosed: but the court issued a warning against the excessive consumption of soda-water.

reasonable force to eject him. The charge of assault, then, falls to the ground.

There remains the question of slander. The innuendo complained of in the words '*Rather late, aren't you?*' is said to be that the plaintiff had been late—illegally late—in terminating the sale of intoxicating liquor. This being a criminal offence it is not necessary for the plaintiff to prove special damage, if the words can be thought to carry a defamatory meaning. I rule that they can, that they were defamatory, and, in fact, untrue. Then there was the remark about 'starting to booze when I've gone.' The plaintiff is rightly jealous for his reputation. In his business he has to be. Lord Mildew said, in *Lott* v. *The Great Western Railway*, 'It is easier to become a priest than a publican.' A licensed victualler must be able to show a blameless record for seven years, and every year his licence must be renewed by the justices. A whisper of wrong-doing may cost him his position. The plaintiff says that the defendant, by his remarks, suggested to those present, many of them men from another borough, that his was a house where the law was habitually and shamelessly broken. Again, since such an accusation affects him in his way of business, no proof of special damage is required. Mr. Lowder's action must succeed, and I award damages of £1,000. The constable will pay all the costs in both cases. I am glad they came before me. Things have come to a pretty pass if police officers can go up to innocent citizens and tell them they are 'late,' especially if, by Greenwich Mean Time, it is only twenty-to-ten. As Lord Mildew said in *Stannaway* v. *Miles*, 'There is not yet a law about going to bed.'

20 June, 1951

(19) THE MERCHANTS' CASE

DOES MAGNA CARTA MATTER?

THE Judicial Committee of the Privy Council on June 1 gave their decision in the Merchants' Case.

The Lord Chancellor said:

In this important case we have to answer an unusual question. Under Section 4 of the Statute of 1833 it is open to His Majesty to refer to us any matter which he thinks fit, whether that matter has been the subject of litigation or not. It is a rare power, but on occasions has proved its usefulness: and this, I think, may be another.

The question is whether certain provisions of the Finance Bill, 1951, are in conflict with Chapter 30 of Magna Carta. An academic question, admittedly—indeed, in a sense, a hypothetical question—for the Finance Bill has not yet become law: and no man can tell exactly in what form it will be presented for the Royal Assent.

On the other hand—and this consideration, I am sure, was in the mind of His Majesty, and the Attorney-General, who advised him—the last chapter of Magna Carta is very clear about the nature and effects of a conflict such as has been posited in argument before us. The Great Charter, that chapter relates, 'was bought from the Crown with a fifteenth of our movable property' . . . in consideration of which the King grants 'for us and our heirs, that neither we nor our heirs shall *attempt*'—note the word—'to do anything whereby the liberties contained in this charter may be infringed or broken. And if anything should be done to the contrary, it shall be held of no force and effect.'

'It shall be held of no force and effect,' the Lord Chancellor repeated gravely. That, no doubt, was a too optimistic assertion: for no British Parliament can be bound by those who came before, as His Majesty's Ministers showed very firmly two years ago concerning the pledges made to the Dominion of Newfoundland by their predecessors in 1933. But no loyal citizen can contemplate without dismay the possibility of the Finance Act, or anything in it, after due consideration by Parliament, receiving the Royal Assent, if it is evidently inconsistent with an important chapter, not repealed, of the Great Charter. Better far, upon an authoritative warning of such a conflict, for the King's Ministers to withdraw their proposals, to abandon the 'attempt,' before they, and Parliament, are irrevocably committed. That I take to be sufficient justification for these unusual proceedings.

Now Chapter 30 of the Great Charter says, wisely and generously, as follows:

All merchants (if they were not openly prohibited before) shall have their safe and sure conduct to depart out of England, to come into England, to tarry in and go through England, as well by land as by water, to buy and sell without any manner of evil tolls (that is, extortions) except in time of war.

The passage which follows deals with the treatment of foreign merchants in time of war: but it is clear that the words I have read cover 'all' merchants, English or foreign. Not only their freedom of movement, but their freedom from 'evil tolls' is guaranteed, as a recognition of the importance of their activities and their advantage to the realm.

The importance of those who 'buy and sell' is hardly less to-day. Indeed, without them starvation would descend upon this island in quick time. Nor is it any less desirable that foreign merchants should be free to bring their merchandise or their money into the country and take it away if they are so inclined. But in the Finance Bill new restrictions upon the free movement of 'merchants,' in the wide sense which ought to be given to the word, are proposed. By Clause 32 it is made unlawful for 'a body corporate resident in the United Kingdom to cease to be so resident' and 'for the trade or business, or any part of the trade or business of a body corporate so resident to be transferred from that body corporate to a person not so resident.' Any person concerned in such an offence may be savagely punished by two years' imprisonment or a fine of ten thousand pounds, or both.

Now, it was powerfully argued before us, by Mr. Albert Haddock among others, that these provisions are an infringement—so far only 'attempted,' it is true—of the 'liberties contained in this Charter': and in my opinion that argument ought to prevail. The Attorney-General told us that by going abroad some 'merchants' may pay fewer taxes. But they may also, I suppose, enjoy better food, more beautiful scenery, more attractive music. It does not seem to me to be relevant to the principles in issue. If that is the trouble the remedy is not to reduce the liberties but to reduce the taxes. And what of the foreigner? What inducement will remain to invest his capital and brains and enterprise in this country if, once in, he can never get out? I hold, without doubt, that the penalties named in Clause 32 are 'evil tolls' of the character which the authors of the Great Charter had in mind and, if that clause be forced on to the Statute Book, the Great Charter should be *pro tanto* amended.

While we are considering the Great Charter, I wish to refer to another chapter, Number 14, which is directed against excessive fines:

A freeman shall not be amerced (that is, fined) for a small fault, but after the manner of the fault; and for a great fault after the greatness thereof, saving to him his contenement; and a merchant likewise saving to him his merchandise. . . .

A man's contenement has been defined as that which is absolutely necessary for his support and maintenance, as his tools and instruments of trade. I note in the minds of Ministers, legislators, and even judges, a shocking tendency to forget Chapter 14 of the Great Charter. In these days so many new and subtle offences are created, so many ordinary acts may not be done without a licence, a certificate or a form that the simple citizen may easily become bewildered. The restrictions on the flow of 'currency,' as it is still laughably called, are a good example: the building regulations are another. A man may dimly understand why he must not take more than a few pounds in notes abroad, but not why he may not bring more than £10 of English money, lawfully acquired, back into his own country.[1] Too often, instead of improving the regulations, or making their purpose plain, the authorities impose increasingly savage fines, and those who inflict them, so far from preserving the wrongdoer's contenement, seem to care nothing if they ruin the man. A citizen can be punished more severely to-day for breaking a building or currency regulation than he would be for manslaughter or burglary. I wish to say that if any such sentences are brought before me in any of my numerous capacities I shall declare them null and void according to the provisions of the Great Charter.

There is an opinion, I am well aware, that so little of Magna Carta is left that none of it is left. Indeed, that was the decision of Mr. Justice Lugg in *Rex* v. *Haddock* [1927]. But I have always thought that that case was wrongly decided.

Lords Right and Left, Middle and Off concurred with the Lord Chancellor. The Cabinet, we understand, are considering the position, and drastic amendments may be made to the Finance Bill.

27 June, 1951

NOTE: No amendments were made; and the Section complained of is now the law of the land. Mr. H. G. Strauss (Norwich, South) put down an amendment to repeal cap. 30 of Magna Carta, but the amendment was not 'called.' On the Third Reading of the Finance Bill (*Hansard*, July 3 1951, Cols. 2,224–5) he said:

'Let us examine what Clause 33 does. First of all, at what companies is it directed? . . . The companies at which Clause 33 is directed are companies which, though resident in the United Kingdom, are trading abroad. That is the important thing to remember: they are trading abroad but they are resident in the United Kingdom. The object of the Clause is to prevent them from leaving the United Kingdom and going abroad, possibly to the country where they are carrying on their trade.

[1] See *Rex* v. *Haddock*, p. 112.

The first thing to realise is that those companies need never have been resident here at all. Why did they choose to be resident here? The answer is, for some of those advantages . . . such as the banking facilities of the City of London, the insurance facilities, shipping and, I might add, the reputation of, and the possibility of access to, English law. All those things made it attractive for them to be resident in the United Kingdom. From that residence the United Kingdom drew immense advantages in invisible exports, which even today constitute one of the main things on which the Chancellor necessarily relies.

'This Clause, then, is directed at companies which are trading abroad and which need never have come here at all. What is the form of the prohibition? It says this:

'All transactions of the following classes . . . shall be unlawful,

unless carried out with the consent of the Treasury. Now let me read the first of those classes of transaction:

'for a body corporate resident in the United Kingdom to cease to be so resident;

That is what the Socialist Government say ought to be prohibited in 1951. I ask hon. Members, with those words fresh in their minds, to remember these words:

'All merchants, if they were not openly prohibited before, shall have their safe and sure conduct to depart out of England, to come into England, to tarry in, and go through England, as well by land as by water, to buy and sell without any manner of evil tolles by the old and rightful customs, except in times of war';

'That is from Magna Carta, 1215. The text can be found in the first volume of the *Statutes Revised*, which any hon. Member can find in either of the Division Lobbies. They will find it in the Statute of Magna Carta of 1297, 25 Edward I, Chapter XXX. That shows the extent of the revolution that is here being enacted and the blindness to the nature of British greatness which the mere putting forward of this Clause involves.'

The Chancellor of the Exchequer said (Col. 2,237):

'In fact, under the Exchange Control Act, so far as the migration of companies is concerned, there has already been existing for the past four years control of the kind to which he objected so much. . . .

I cannot therefore readily accept that all the sinister consequences that the hon. and learned Member seemed to indicate would follow, have any substance whatever, because they certainly have not been apparent in the last few years.'

But, in that case, Magna Carta should have been amended four years ago.

(20) REX *v.* GENTLE, GOOD AND HADDOCK

'PAYING TO RULE'
(Before a Divisional Court)

MR. JUSTICE HORNET, giving judgment in this enthralling case, said:

The defendants, Gentle, Good and Haddock, are charged with offences against Section One of the Finance (New Duties) Act, 1916. That Act, for the purpose of raising new revenue for the temporary[1] purposes of war, accepted the barbarous principle of a tax upon amusement. 'No persons,' it said, 'shall be admitted to any entertainment except

'(*a*) with a ticket stamped with a stamp (not before used) denoting that the proper Entertainment Duty has been paid, or

'(*b*) in special cases, with the approval of the Commissioners, through a barrier which, or by means of a mechanical contrivance which, automatically registers the number of persons admitted.'

Theatres, as a rule, do not employ turnstiles; the business of affixing stamps to tickets was tiresome; manpower was precious: so, in the circumstances of war, there was a third arrangement. Theatrical managers and other 'entertainers' were permitted to give security that they would keep an exact account of the numbers of persons admitted and hand over the appropriate tax at the end of the week. This was a great convenience for the Board of Customs and Excise. They did not have to provide stamps or (except for an occasional visit by an inspector) officials. The managers did the Crown's work for it. For them it was a great labour, and required very often an increase of staff. Moreover, since the duty was included in the price of the tickets, the arrangement concealed

[1] Ha!—ED.

from many of the public the extent of the tax, and the managers were blamed for high prices which were really the work of the Crown. Yet these toils and troubles were cheerfully endured by patriotic men. What is more surprising is that when the war was concluded, and the 'temporary' tax continued, they still sheepishly co-operated with the perfidious State, and have done so ever since.

In the present year, according to the evidence, there has been a change. One of those unpredictable gusts of spontaneous feeling familiar to the student of affairs has swept through the entertainment world as an April gale blows through the forest. Each branch of entertainment, it seems, has a different grievance. In the cinema, at a time of exceptional difficulty, the tax has been increased in the present year. In the theatre, objection is expressed to an arrangement by which some theatres pay no tax at all. Football and billiards pay at a lower rate because they are 'live' entertainments, but motor-bicycle racing is not so indulged. Circuses pay at one rate and horse-racing at another. The defendant Gentle, for the greyhound racing world, expressed a particular grievance against the State. Dog-racing, with 'live' dogs, it seems, pays entertainments tax at the full rate, and in addition a betting tax is levied upon the dog-race course which is not levied upon the horse-race course, or anywhere else.

These complaints do not concern the Court except as an atmospherical background to the case. They all had one result. The defendant Good, we are told, wrote to the Board of Customs and Excise as follows: 'I am producing a play called *Hamlet* at the —— Theatre. The State, I understand, desires to levy a tax on the tickets of all those admitted to see it. Very well. The State is supreme. But I am a theatrical manager, not a tax-collector. Let the State collect its own —— taxes! From Thursday next pray send your officers to the Stalls, Dress Circle, Upper Circle, Pit and Gallery entrances of this theatre (at 6.45 Mon. to Sat., and 2.15 Wed. and Sat.), ready to affix the appropriate stamps to any tickets I may sell. This will be a nuisance to our public, but it cannot be helped. At least they will realize where their money is going, and the odium of the tax will fall where it should.'

Mr. Gentle wrote, not less robustly: 'Next Saturday we are having a greyhound race-meeting at the Stadium. We are loyal citizens doing our best to give pleasure to the people, pay our due taxes, and make an honest living. But the State has given us so little consideration that we see no reason why we should cosset the State. We are tired of doing sums for the State and we can no longer afford the extra staff. Let the State do its own dirty work. Pray send officials (with stamps) to the twenty-six entrances of the Stadium in good time on Saturday —also to the many other race-courses controlled by this Association, a list of which is appended. *L'État—ce n'est pas moi.*'

These two letters, by themselves, might have caused no great anxiety at the fine Customs House at Billingsgate: but, as I have said, a kind of contagious fever was abroad. Entertainers of every kind sent similar letters in the same week from every city and corner of the realm: and it may well be that the Board of Customs and Excise, in these days of full employment, was unable to furnish officials sufficient to meet the very numerous demands. Accordingly, by his own account, the defendant Haddock, having purchased an expensive stalls ticket for the play called *Hamlet*, waited in vain at the head of an eager queue for an Excise official to stamp his ticket. It never entered his mind, he told the Court, to enter the auditorium with an unstamped ticket, for he is, he says, an unusually law-abiding subject. But, when the orchestra was heard, the pressure of the impatient people behind him was too much for him, and he was swept unwillingly into the stalls. A similar misfortune befell him two days later when, through no fault of his own, he found himself watching the dog-races with an unstamped ticket.

Now, the Crown says that in both these cases he is 'liable to an Excise Penalty' of £50 as a 'person admitted' contrary to the Act, and that the defendants Good and Gentle are each liable to the same penalty as 'the proprietors' of the entertainments to which he was 'admitted.'

The answer of the defence is simple. They say that he was not 'admitted'; that both he and the proprietors did all that could reasonably be expected of them to prevent his 'admission'; that he was forced into the theatre, and into the dog arena, by the irresistible pressure of the crowd: and that for that pressure the Crown itself was responsible by its failure to provide sufficient officers to stamp the tickets lawfully sold and purchased.

The Crown says that it was the duty of the proprietors to stamp the tickets. But for that contention the Court has been unable to find any support in law. There is nothing in the original Act, or in the numerous regulations made under it, which commands the proprietor in every case to affix the stamp (there is an exception where tickets are issued in 'books or sheets' and the tickets pass out of the proprietors' control). It would be surprising if it were otherwise. Many Customs and Excise Duties are collected every day at our sea-ports. If the Customs officers failed to be present to collect what was due from the passengers of a home-coming ship, no one would expect the shipowner to do their duty for them, and no Court would condemn a passenger who, after searching vainly for a Customs officer, entered the waiting train and proceeded to his home with his dutiable goods. The parallel seems to me to be exact. The Crown is wrong.

Mr. Justice Codd said: I agree. But I wish to add a word or two. It may be that after this decision the Excise Commissioners will seek to escape from their difficulties by making a regulation requiring the proprietors to stamp the tickets in every case. I may say at once that in my opinion such a regulation would be *ultra vires* and of no effect. Tax-collection is the business of the Crown, and if Parliament desires these serious powers and duties to be handed over to private citizens it will, without doubt, clearly say so, as it has in some affairs, but not in this. For one thing, the tax-collector is worthy of his hire, and must be remunerated like the rest of us. The case is dismissed.

25 July, 1951

(21) REX *v.* HADDOCK; HADDOCK *v.* REX

THE House of Lords to-day laid down a new principle of
law in this important case.

The Lord Chancellor said:

This charming morsel of litigation would not, in the ordinary
course, have reached your Lordships' table. It was sent up to
us by the rough but sensible procedure first used in the misleading case of *Board of Inland Revenue* v. *Haddock*, 1931.[1] A
succession of courts below, apprehending at a glance that being
bound by previous decisions they were unable to determine
the matter except in a manner repugnant to natural justice,
declined to waste their time and talents on a full hearing but
remitted the case *quam celerrime* to this, the highest tribunal in
the land.

Not for the first time, a high question of law has sprung
from the lowly, and sometimes squalid, affairs of Mr. Albert
Haddock. In this case that tenacious litigant and friend of
freedom, returning from Australia in the Orient Line steamer
Orchid, was examined as usual at the port of landing in this
country by the customs and immigration authorities. When
asked how much English currency he had in his possession he
answered frankly that he had about £80 in what are still
amusingly known as British 'pound notes.' At this information,
according to the evidence, one of the examining officers
fainted. Another, with a white face, asked Mr. Haddock
whether he was not aware of some regulation made under the
Exchange Control Act, 1947, the exact title and number of
which I confess I forget myself. It is—or was, at that time, it
appears—ordained by this bizarre regulation that no British
subject should leave these shores with more than £5 in British

[1] See Note, p. 115.

currency, and, stranger still, should not return with more than the same amount. (The figure, I have been informed, has since been graciously raised to £10.)[1] Mr. Haddock said that he was well aware of the regulation, but added rashly that he had never regarded it as worthy of serious consideration and in this case found it impossible to observe. 'So,' he added, in an idiom which is new to this House, 'what?'

The officers, shocked, it seems, as much by his *insouciance* as by his offence, confiscated 75 of his £80, and he was prosecuted and fined for a breach of the regulations. He has appealed. He also wants his money back.

In evidence, he painted a vivid picture of the last days in a great British liner returning to the mother country. The passengers, he said, have incurred various financial obligations; wine-bills, bar-bills, laundry-bills, radio-bills, besides the tips which will be expected by many obliging stewards. To meet these numerous calls they cash their Travellers' Cheques: but the calls are not always easy to assess exactly, and their minds are haunted by the fear of error. If they draw out too little money they may be confronted as they go ashore, when it is too late to draw any more, by the sad reproachful face of some steward they have forgotten or have insufficiently rewarded. If, on the other hand, they draw too much there is the menace of the regulation already mentioned. Those who through inadvertence, or faulty arithmetic, have more than £5 when all their obligations are discharged, must somehow get rid of the unlawful excess; and it appears that unnecessary and wasteful drinking is almost the only practical way out. Deplorable scenes, described by Mr. Haddock, are directly due, he says, to the regulation; and many a young person has been set on the downward path to drink through having a few pounds more than the law of Britain permits them to 'import.'

During these last days an Australian friend expressed a desire to purchase a very fine and elaborate camera belonging

[1] 'There should be a new term for "currency." A current moves freely. Money, in these days, does not' (Lord Mildew in *Bank of England* v. *Thomas Cook* (1949), 2 A.C.).

to Mr. Haddock. That gentleman was uneasily aware of the unjust and merciless demands which would be made upon him by way of income and other taxes the moment he reached his native land: and he consented, with some reluctance, to the sale. The price fixed was £80. The Australian insisted—and Mr. Haddock agreed—that the price should be paid in English Treasury notes. How the Australian, a sheep-farmer, came to be in possession of so much United Kingdom currency is not clear. One suggestion is that he had betted heavily and successfully on the 'Ship's Run' throughout the long voyage. But that does not concern us. No doubt he heard about the regulation, and, as a stranger, was eager to conform with the law. Mr. Haddock, on the other hand, could not suppose, as he told us, that there could be any serious objection to a transaction so evidently advantageous to his own country. There may be good and obvious reasons for forbidding the citizen to take more than a fixed sum in English money out of the country: but who can condemn the man who goes forth into the world with £5 only, and by the exercise of legitimate commercial enterprise, comes back with £80? Great would have been the surprise of Drake, of Raleigh, and Cook, if after long voyages their Monarch had received them in such a manner. The learned Attorney-General, by the way, somewhat half-heartedly I thought, suggested that it was not a legitimate transaction, that Mr. Haddock should not have sold the camera without an Export Licence. Mr. Haddock replied that the article was sold in a British ship approaching British shores, and is in this island at the present time, so that it can hardly be said to have been exported. I think that he is right.

There, then, the ugly matter rests. The country is richer by £75. Mr. Haddock, the author of the increment, has been placed in the dock and fined, and his innocent gains have been taken from him. In the long history of State rapacity and harsh dealing I can recall few episodes like it. Counsel for the Crown, with the familiar Treasury shrug, say 'It is the law' and leave it at that. That, too, must be enough for lesser courts than this. But we, my Lords, guarding the supreme fount of justice, must be sure that the well is pure. We have endeavoured earnestly to ascertain the point and purpose of the regulation. Civil Servants of high character and advanced years were summoned from the gloomy dens of the Treasury. They mumbled through their beards the mystic formula 'Currency Control.' They whispered that the regulation had been first devised in time of war, when it must have had some purpose, but they could not remember what— 'something,' one muttered, 'about Black Market.' They admitted that if Mr. Haddock had sold the camera in Australia and sent the money home through a bank all would have been well: but they could not explain what important difference arose when the money came to London in notes. I suspect that the regulation has been allowed to survive in times of peace through sheer inertia or pure love of control. But, for your Lordships' House, I take it, there is no special magic in the words 'Currency Control.' Whether or not, in general, there is something to be said for the regulation we cannot discover. As applied and enforced in this particular case it appears to me to be nonsense. Your Lordships ought never to be asked to give their blessing and support to non-sensical regulations masquerading as law: and I hope they will never consent. If Parliament originates and carefully passes through all its stages an imbecile Act of Parliament, that is one thing. It is the law, and must be upheld. The whimsical edicts of Whitehall worthies deserve, and will receive, much less respect. To them, I suggest, we should apply a new maxim— '*Lex non stultitiam admittit.*' In the light of that maxim, Mr. Haddock's conviction should be quashed, he should get his money back, and I recommend that a sum of *about* £1,000 be paid to him out of the public funds by way of compensation for grievous injustice and loss of sleep.

Lords Right and Left, Lords Wool and Strawberry, agreed. Lord Strawberry thought that £2,000 would be more like it.

17 October, 1951

NOTE: In *Board of Inland Revenue* v. *Haddock* (1931) to which the Lord Chancellor referred, the Master of the Rolls delivered his celebrated judgment on the appellate system: 'The institution of one Court of Appeal may be considered a reasonable precaution; but two suggest panic. To take a fair parallel, our great doctors, I think, could not claim to be more respected or more advanced in their own science than our greatest jurists. But our surprise would be great if, after the removal of an appendix by a distinguished surgeon, we were taken before three other distinguished surgeons, who ordered our appendix to be replaced: and our surprise would give place to stupefaction if we were then referred to a tribunal of seven distinguished surgeons, who directed that our appendix should be extracted again. Yet such operations, or successions of operations, are an everyday experience in the practice of the law. . . . The people can be taught to believe in one Court of Appeal; but when there are two they cannot be blamed if they believe in neither. When a man keeps two clocks which tell the time differently, his fellows will receive with suspicion his weightiest pronouncements upon the hour of the day, even if one of them happens to be right. Moreover, the expense of successive appeals must make the acquisition of justice difficult for the rich and impossible for the poor. The unsuccessful litigant who cannot afford to go beyond the Court of Appeal must always be haunted by the thought that in the House of Lords he might have won; while the Inland Revenue, relying on the public purse, can pursue their unjust claims to the end and, if they lose, can send the bill to the taxpayer.

'For all these reasons we recommend that either this Court or the House of Lords (as a Court of Appeal) be abolished: or, in the alternative, that the House of Lords retain its appellate functions as a specialist body for the settlement of questions of exceptional difficulty, such cases to be referred to them upon the order of a High Court judge. As for the present case, we decline to discuss it. It will go to the House of Lords in any event, so let it go at once.'

(22) ALBERT AND GLORIA HADDOCK v. THE KING

WHOSE PASSPORT IS YOURS?

THE House of Lords to-day determined this appeal from a decision of the Court of Appeal reversing (Merry L. J. dissenting) a judgment of Dandrough J. in the King's Bench Division.

The Lord Chancellor said:

Your Lordships are well acquainted with one of the appellants, that patient apostle of liberty and good sense Mr. Albert Haddock. But this is the first time, I think, that his help-meet, Gloria, has come into Court with him. We bid her welcome and will do what we can for her.

This important appeal concerns the nature of a passport and the property in a passport; and the rights, if any, of the Crown to restrict the movements of the citizen in time of peace. Mr. Haddock's passport is of the fine old vintage of the late Mr. Ernest Bevin. It 'requests and requires in the name of His Majesty' that Mr. Haddock may be allowed 'to pass freely without let or hindrance.' It is stated to be 'valid' till a date five years from the date of issue. On the last page there is a wise cautionary note, reminding the holder that the passport is '*a valuable document*' and 'should not be allowed to pass into the possession of an unauthorized person.' But what, one wonders, is meant by 'an unauthorized person'?

Note, also, my Lords, in passing, the words 'valuable document.' It is certainly that, for, to obtain it, Mr. Haddock had to pay a sum of money to the State.

Now, in the present year, *consule* Morrison, Mrs. Haddock had occasion to acquire a new passport, in order to travel with her husband abroad. He assisted her in the prolonged formalities and paid the money demanded by the Passport Office. But Gloria's passport was 'new' in more senses than one.

'What' says Mr. Haddock (page 4375 in the transcript of evidence) 'was my astonishment to find (on the last page, before the usual caution about the "valuable document") the following entirely novel statement:

    ' "*This passport remains the property of His Majesty's Government and may be withdrawn at any time.*" '

There is nothing to that effect in Albert's passport: but it appears that the passport of Mr. Haddock's son, of an intermediate vintage, has a different formula. This one '*may be withdrawn if the holder ceases to be entitled to the protection of His Majesty's Government.*'

Now it is clear, as Mr. Haddock maintains, that in this land of equality a husband and wife can hardly hold two passports of different status or quality. If Gloria's passport belongs to the Crown, so does Albert's.

The appellants, therefore, have asked for a declaration (*a*) that their passports are their own property, duly acquired for value, or (*b*) in the alternative, that the Crown has obtained money from them by false pretences, and should restore it.

My Lords, if you please, I will discuss the second point first. The money-claim is small in amount (fifteen shillings) and by some may be considered squalid in character. But in my opinion it throws a powerful light on the constitutional point which is at the heart of this case. The Crown, with the citizens' assistance, prepares—and 'issues'—many official documents: the Birth Certificate, the Motor, Dog, Game or Radio Licence, the Ration Card, the Identity Card, the National Health Insurance Card. For some of these it charges a fee; for others not. Any citizen, I think, would be greatly surprised to hear that any of these documents were not his 'property,' especially one for which he had paid a fee. On his Identity Card, for which no charge is made, he is told what to do if he finds a card 'not *belonging* to him.' There are legislative provisions for the suspension or cancellation by a court of law of a driving licence where offences have been committed.

But no one, surely, would suggest that the Crown, that is, a Government Department, would be entitled to 'withdraw' a Birth Certificate (for which one penny is charged) or a Dog Licence 'at any time,' that is, without showing cause in some process of law. That, though, is what the Crown claims in relation to the passport. They make it, on an early page, in prominent type, 'Valid for five years.' In small type, on the last page, they say that it is Government property, and can be taken away to-morrow. If the citizen's rights in the document are indeed so small and fleeting it is surprising, and possibly fraudulent, that he should be made to pay fifteen shillings for them.

But are his rights so small? At a day not very distant, but now almost forgotten, the passport was not required at all for travel in normal conditions in civilized lands. But it could be demanded as a right by any good citizen who proposed to travel in dangerous times and regions, and thought that a good word from His Majesty's Government might assist him whether with British or foreign officials. Wars came; the world was more difficult and dangerous; and the passport slowly grew into an instrument more for the restriction than the assistance of movement. But still the *prima facie right* to the passport remained: and the passport could only be 'withdrawn,' as we have seen, where the holder 'ceased to be entitled to the protection of His Majesty's Government'—or, in other words, was guilty of some grave offence, to his own country, or perhaps another.

The new formula, on the latest breed of passport—and let it be noted that there are now three differently worded forms of passport in currency—goes very much farther. It can be 'withdrawn' (whatever that means) 'at any time,' not because the holder 'has ceased to deserve His Majesty's protection,' but because the Foreign Secretary does not like his face, or thinks that he should not waste his time and money on holidays abroad. But this is to turn a right into a privilege; a security into a gamble; an open door into a barricade. For though, so far as I know, there is still no law,

or even regulation, which ordains that a man may not pass
from England to France without a passport, in practice he
will not get far without one, unless he travels in a yacht. A
railway company might as well announce that, having sold
a ticket, it is entitled to take it away at once.

It is highly important, therefore, that your Lordships'
House should determine, once for all, the question of property.
If a private citizen took Mr. Haddock's passport, he could
without doubt proceed against him, as if the man had taken his
watch—or his Birth Certificate. Suppose that the Crown asks
Mr. Haddock to surrender his passport, and Mr. Haddock
refuses. Can the Crown send a policeman to take away his
passport by force? I think not. For there is nothing in any Act
of Parliament, or, so far as I know, any Statutory Regulation
or Order that gives the Crown that power. They have sold
this document, for value received, and it is now the personal
property of Mr. Haddock. After five years it may lose its
'validity' but, unless he wants to acquire another, no-one can
compel him to hand it over.[1] If the State has any good reason
for wishing to stop him travelling, the State, no doubt, will
find some good way of doing so.

From this decision many small but valuable results may
follow. All over the world innumerable officials are making a
living by defacing Mr. Haddock's passport with what are
known as 'stamps.' These are often illegible, and their purpose
and justification is seldom plain. If, as I have declared, the
passport is Mr. Haddock's personal property, all this stamping,
it is clear, amounts to a trespass unless Mr. Haddock agrees to
it: and if all the Mr. Haddocks united in objecting much time
and trouble and money would be saved. It follows too that the
modern practice in certain countries by which the traveller's
passport is taken away from him for inspection by the police
and others must be contrary to law. For no Government is
entitled to take a Briton's property away from him.

---

[1] The police or the Official Receiver may *ask* the citizen to surrender his
passport as a condition of the granting of bail or an earnest of good intentions, but, *quaere*, they can do nothing if he refuses.

I therefore find for Mr. Haddock and his lady. The appeal should be allowed, and a declaration made in the terms demanded.[1]

Lords Right, Wool, Strawberry and Bindweed concurred.

24 October, 1951

NOTE: See also a lively paper on 'Passportery' read at the 18th Congress of Indignant Travellers (*Sunday Times*, September 15, 1951):

The persecutions of passportery have increased, are increasing and ought to be diminished. It is about a quarter of a century since we observed that the passport, designed to allow us 'to pass freely, without let or hindrance' is, in fact, the cause of more lets and hindrances than anything else. Things are much worse now, and, here and there, they seem to gather new evil every year. The nerves of the globe are worse, it is true, and its future seems even less assured than in 1925. But the disturbing suspicion grows that passportery has very little practical purpose except the maintenance of full employment among the passport tribes.

A journey by train from Marseilles (France) to Barcelona (Spain) sounded fairly simple. But then we had not heard of Port Bou, the frontier station. (It is, we have since heard, a name of major ill-omen, even among frontier towns.)

At the station before it, at 0630, our passport was stamped by a Frenchman and a Spaniard, and we filled in the first form. This was a four-page affair about the money we possessed. We counted laboriously our own surviving cheques and our grubby packets of French and Spanish paper. We wrote the results down, in pencil, on the wrong page, and added, without resentment, for it was a fine warm morning, the number of our passport, where and by whom it was *expedido*, and so forth. We signed our declaration grandly, the train started, and we observed then that the whole thing should be *escrito en tinta*, the quaint old Spanish word for ink. We pitied the poor

---

[1] See a letter to the *Sunday Times*, September 30, 1951:

'In 1945 many passports were issued free of charge to persons taking up posts on the Control Commission for Germany (of whom I was one).

'On returning to the U.K. I was informed by the Foreign Office that my passport was not my property but would become so on payment of 15s. As it is now once more the property of His Majesty's Government, I have asked the passport office to refund my 15s.

'J. W. NIXON.'

'*Geneva.*'

I

traveller who had no Spanish (or no fountain-pen) and hastily inked over our pencilled information. The train joggled, our fountain-pen spluttered and oozed, and the form looked fairly fishy when we had done. But we approached the Spanish frontier with a light heart. After all, we had His Majesty's passport, showing that Britain thought well of us: we had presented two photographs and a mass of information to the Spaniards in London, and they had given us a *visa*. If these documents meant anything, there would be one swift glance and we should be through.

But we did not know Port Bou. Our fellow-travellers were nearly all Italian, French or Spanish. From time to time, in the loud and excitable talk so deplorably common on the Continent, we caught the word *maquis*, and once we heard '*mucha batalla!*' That seemed to be the mood of our companions. They had no queue-discipline. Indeed, there were no queues—only scrums: and there were some heavy-weight women who could have got a cap for almost any country. We think the British do passportery best. At least, you are clearly directed or ushered from one operation to another and herded into narrow tracks where shoving does no good. Here it was a pure fluke if you found yourself in the right scrum.

We have heard since of travellers being driven near to madness at Port Bou. The lady next to us at the Customs counter was not far off it. She had just heard about the *tinta* and had no fountain-pen (and why should travellers be compelled to carry fountain-pens?). We nobly lent her ours and waited a long time while she scribbled on the top of a squashy bag.

Done with the Customs, we noticed two large sweating and shouting scrums outside two tiny windows labelled Exchange of Money. We did not want to change any money, so we marched confidently on to the next door. 'Show the passport,' we thought, 'and we are through.' But they waved us back towards the scrums. '*Banco—banco!*' they said. By sheer brutality and rudeness we fought our way at last to the little window. The owl in the window gazed solemnly at the 'declaration' page of our money form and stamped it. He also stamped our passport. But since we had failed to put anything about money over our signature our 'declaration' declared nothing but our name and the number of our passport. In other words, the form was meaningless—but it did not matter. It was stamped, just the same.

We marched on to the gate and showed our passport. 'Through at at last?' 'No.' The man simply handed us a form and indicated yet one more scrum. The form required us to state—*en tinta*—nearly all the information contained in our passport—when and where it was issued—date and place of *visa*—age—place of birth—nationality—domicile—profession—address—the whole box of tricks. The small room was full of luggage, porters, and yelling passengers, sharing fountain-pens. The near-mad lady was now practically raving, for her glasses had fallen off and broken in one of the scrums and she could not see the form. An interpreter took charge of her and we suppose she is now in a Home. Half-way through our own form our fountain-pen ran dry and we had to borrow. A porter cried that the train was due to leave *pronto*. We plunged into the scrum round a little window labelled *Pasaporte Controle*. When we touched down a scruffy little owl turned over a page or two of our passport, looked wise, and stamped it again—the fourth stamp that happy morning. We just caught the train, but there was no time for so much as a cup of coffee. It was a horrible little one-waggon train which rolled like a destroyer for three hours to Barcelona. But such are the fortunes of travel. At least we were in Spain—*Spain!*—and all passportery done. We admired the sunny hills and valleys of Catalonia. We almost admired the unshaven little man in the light-blue suit who rolled and sweated opposite to us. But presently he rose up and went round the waggon asking all passengers to show their passports. We did. He had no uniform. *Dios* knows who he was and what was his authority. Perhaps it was a joke. But our spirit was broken; and no one asked him.

We reached our hotel in Barcelona in very fair fettle, still one of the Friends of Spain, though we had not eaten or drunk for sixteen hours. The hotel at once (*a*) took away our passport, to send to the police, and (*b*) handed us a huge form, requiring, once more, *all the information contained in our passport*. At this point, we did begin to wonder what our passport was for.

On this short passage into Spain:

(*a*) our passport had been stamped four times;

(*b*) our passport had been presented seven times;

(*c*) we had filled up two forms giving all the particulars already set out in our passport, and one giving a few of them: and at the end of all this

(*d*) our passport was taken away and sent to the police—'for checking.'

Can all this be really necessary to the safety of any State—however nervous? True, our passport came back quickly: but why did it go at all? It should be part of the Law of Nations that an innocent traveller's passport must never be taken from him. While he is without it he may get into a row, or fall under a bus—and then he is lost. And why, if they take our passport, must they have the form as well? Both cannot be needed. What is checking what? Is it supposed that a villain holding a false passport would be so foolish as to copy out the particulars erroneously? And what happens to the form we filled up at the frontier? That perhaps is 'checked' at last with the form we filled up at the hotel. But, by that time, we may have left the country. And what, in any case, can the operation tell them except that we have said the same thing three times? This persecution is not even practical. We are told that by this system the Spanish authorities are supposed to know where all foreigners are: but when a Briton disappeared, a British Consul told us, the Spanish with all their forms were quite unable to trace him. In spite of all the forms a 'missing diplomat' cannot be caught. Crooks and criminals 'pass freely, without let or hindrance.' The innocent traveller is harried and robbed.

The Nations may not be able to agree about the big things: but could they not get together about the little ones? We suggest the following resolution for this great Conference:

'Except in special circumstances of emergency or suspicion
(1) Each State shall treat with respect the passport of another State—and its own *visas*.
(2) The passport is the inviolable property of the individual.'

From this would follow a lot. All round the planet there are thousands of scrubby unshaven little men gazing with suspicion at our passports (and their own visas). They turn the pages and look profoundly wise. Then comes the condescending stamp. But they have seen nothing. We do not believe that a single thought is in their minds: except perhaps 'After this lot we shall have a good breakfast,' or 'This is a good job. I must keep it.' Accept our resolution, and most of these gentlemen could be removed to some more productive toil.

The passport is an excellent thing: but *Pasaporte Controle* has gone too far.

(23) TEMPER *v.* HUME AND HADDOCK

SLANDER AT SEA

SIR ELIOT EMBER, K.C., to-day concluded his final speech for the plantiff in this protracted case: and the aged Mr. Justice Codd, shortly to retire, began his summing-up to the jury:

This difficult case, he said, has, I think, no fellow in the history of litigation. For one thing, it is, so far as I know, the first action for defamation in which the words complained of were conveyed by flag-signals at sea. It was suggested, at one point, that the case should be transferred to the Admiralty Court: and, though I had to say No, I have regretted it more than once, so unfamiliar are the waters in which we find ourselves.

The plaintiff, Temper, is the owner and master of the motor-yacht *Perfume II*. The defendant Hume is owner and master of the motor-yacht *Iodine*. The defendant Haddock was a passenger, or rather a guest, in the *Iodine*. Both vessels were cruising in the Mediterranean. At their first encounter in a crowded Italian harbour (X——) there was, it seems, a childish, unseemly and unnecessary altercation between the plaintiff and the defendant Hume. The details do not greatly concern you: but you may well form the opinion, on the evidence you have heard, that the plaintiff was in the wrong, that he was angry and ill-mannered, without due cause: and it is common ground that when the dispute was over he went out of his way to send by boat an insulting message. Mr. Hume, it seems, a man of dignity and calm, thought the insult no more worthy of notice than the buzzing of an inflated blue-bottle, and throughout behaved with good humour and gentleness. But, his friend and guest, Mr. Haddock, less forgiving than the Owner, thought that the last word should not be left where it lay. Hence this action-at-law.

Mr. Haddock, as he told the Court, has long been an admiring student of the International Code of flag-signals. This great Code, begun in a small way by our own Captain Marryat, is one of the many fine marine affairs in which our country has led the way, got the nations together, and benefited the world. It is now so copious and well-planned that almost any thought that one ship can reasonably wish to express to another is provided for. It ranges from the short sharp one-flag signals such as the famous 'Blue Peter' (P), or K—'You should stop your vessel instantly'—to such complex queries as

LVI 'Can you suggest any means whereby my radio apparatus could be made serviceable?'

Mr. Haddock thinks that the Code should be better known, and more commonly used, than it is, especially by small yachts on the high seas. Instead, for example, of fumbling vainly round the dial of a crackling 'wireless,' seeking the weather-report in a foreign language, they should, he says, steer close to the nearest big steamer (whatever her nationality) and hoist the two flags:

ZB 'What is the weather forecast for to-day?

to which the steamer will reply:

YV 'Heavy weather coming: take necessary precautions.'
or
ATI 'There is no need for alarm.'

or whatever it may be.

Instead, he said, of laborious morsing with lamps which suddenly cease to work or cannot be clearly distinguished, two or three gaily coloured flags will often do what is wanted quicker and better—as, for example:

OVG 'Thank-you'
or
WAY 'I wish you a pleasant, happy voyage'.

But, he said—and all this is more relevant to the case than you may at once perceive—practice makes perfect, and custom grows with use. Accordingly, he has often sent messages to other yachts and steamers which were not made absolutely necessary by any marine emergency. Not all these communications, it appears, were uniformly well-timed. On one occasion, he confessed, passing the *Queen Elizabeth* in mid-Channel, he hoisted with all solemnity the three groups:

GSX 'Good'
JMR 'Morning.'
QUH 'Have you any women on board?'

On another occasion, in war-time, as assistant to the Commodore of a Convoy, he persuaded the Commodore to send to all the merchant ships, in 29 hoists, the whole of the famous peroration of Mr. Churchill which begins 'Let us therefore brace ourselves to our duties' and ends 'This was their finest hour.' How these communications were received by the masters of the vessels addressed we do not know; but you may think that Mr. Temper was not the first mariner to complain of Mr. Haddock's fondness for the International Code.

I pass now to the facts of the case. The yachts *Perfume II* and *Iodine* met again frequently, sometimes at sea, sometimes in the many harbours which all yachts seem to visit, sooner or later, in the Western Mediterranean. While passing the *Perfume*, a much slower vessel, Mr. Haddock got permission from Mr. Hume to 'practise with the flags': and he hoisted the first signal complained of:

IBQ 'Do you know'
RLO 'Rules of the Road at Sea?'

The plaintiff regarded this as an offensive reference to the former encounter, but could think of no adequate reply in flags. That signal was followed by:

LWV 'Have dead rats been found on board?'

The plaintiff, as you have heard, angrily seized an Aldis lamp and began a strongly-worded reply in morse. The defendant Haddock sent up two hoists:

WX   'I cannot stop to communicate with you.'
LVE   'You should use radio.'

And the *Iodine* steamed ahead.

When the *Perfume* arrived in the crowded little harbour of Y—— the *Iodine* was flying, as if by way of welcome, the distinguishing flags of the *Perfume*, and the signal:

LWV   'Have dead rats been found on board?'

The plaintiff called on the *Iodine* and expostulated with Mr. Hume. Mr. Hume said mildly that Mr. Haddock was only 'practising with the flags as usual.' Mr. Haddock, on the other hand, said that he had noticed a dead rat on the quay-side at Port X——, and, when passing the *Perfume* (who was upwind), he had fancied perhaps, a similar smell. Naturally, he had wondered anxiously whether both vessels were threatened by the same infection. But if the flags offended, they should come down at once. And they did.

But in the next port, Z——, there was more trouble. The Code is rich in medical signals. These are designed to assist one ship to describe to another the condition of a sufferer for whom the first ship requires medical aid. The *Perfume II* was greeted, as usual, with LWV, but, this time, paid no attention. On the second night there was a little party in the *Perfume*, rather noisy, rather late. The next morning there appeared at the yard-arm of the *Iodine*, addressed to *Perfume II*, the following signals which, I must say, look jolly gay and satisfactory to me:

AGW   'Group which follows is a question.'
HGQ   'Headache is very severe.'
PCP   'Tongue is coated.'
VGF   'Belly wall is tender.'

The plaintiff again complained.

Mr. Albert Haddock's reply to the complaint was simple. He said that that was how he felt that morning, and, as one mariner to another, he was asking a sympathetic question. This time, the flags were not taken down.

At Port W——, after the routine LWV ('Have dead rats been found on board?'), there was a new and singular set of signals:

AGW 'Group which follows is a question.'
VGI 'Breathing is noisy or snorting.'
VGQ 'Have night sweats.'
VGO 'Eyeball burst.'

At Port V——, it was:

AGW 'Group which follows is a question.'
PCP 'Tongue is coated.'
HGQ 'Headache is very severe.'
PJP 'Troubled.'
CPT 'By.'
ATL 'Alcohol.'

And so on.

Now, gentlemen, it is for you and me to analyse and assess the legal significance of this unusual story of the sea. The plaintiff complains of various *innuendoes* or suggestions in the signals, to wit, that he was unseamanlike, that his ship was plague-ridden or otherwise unhealthy, that he was given to excessive drinking; and he says that he has been held up to hatred, ridicule and contempt in the yachting world. He says that in more than one harbour he was greeted by acquaintances with remarks about 'vermin-vessels' or 'deratization.' I have ruled that certain of the flags might bear a defamatory meaning, and you will have to decide whether in all the circumstances they were defamatory or not.

The next question is: By whom were the statements, if defamatory, made? You will probably find that Mr. Haddock in each case selected and hoisted the flags: but that he did so with the general permission of Mr. Hume, the owner and

master of the vessel. In the case of a newspaper the proprietor,
the editor and the writer of libellous matter may each and all
be sued. But a motor-yacht is not a newspaper (see *The Queen*
v. *Robinson* (1891), 2 Q.B.) The nautical experts who testified
before us were unanimous that a signal flown at the ship's
yard-arm is a signal from the ship, and that, in the absence
of fraud or mutiny, the master is alone responsible. It may be,
then, that whatever you find in fact, I shall have to strike
Mr. Haddock out of the action as a matter of law. A further
difficulty will then present itself, concerning damages.
Whatever you may think about the mind of Mr. Haddock, you
are not likely to find any evidence of malice in the mind of Mr.
Hume, who showed gentlemanly forbearance under great
provocation. There need, it is true, be no evidence of express
malice where a libel is proved, unless the occasion be privi-
leged, which this is not: but you may well think it right to
assess different damages for the two defendants, unjust though
that may seem. Dear me, what a case!

There remains, for me, at least, perhaps the most delicate
question of all. Is this a case of libel or slander? Though the
plaintiff complains that his reputation has suffered, he has
been able to offer no evidence of any actual damage such as
must support, in most cases, an action for slander. He has not
suffered professionally or been turned out of a club. Now, the
historical but crazy distinction between libel and slander is
thus expressed by the good Mr. Salmond (I quote the text-
book because if I began to quote the judges I should be at it
for many days):

> In *libel* the defamatory statement is made in some permanent and
> visible form, such as writing, printing, or effigies. In *slander* it is made
> in spoken words or in some other transitory form, whether visible or
> audible, such as gestures, hissing, or other inarticulate but significant
> sounds.[1]

Very well. Where are we now? What are flags? They are
'visible', like writing, printing, or effigies, but unlike words,

[1] *Law of Torts* (Stevens and Haynes).

whispers, or hisses. So, *prima facie*, they must be libel. But are they 'permanent'? Surely not. At sea, the flags remain at the yard-arm till the receiving ship has hoisted the Answering Pendant to the peak, signifying that the signal is understood. Then the flags come down. Gone like the wind. A 'transitory' defamation, surely. But then the plaintiff has sworn that in some ports the flags complained of remained on view *all day*. Should such an exhibition be regarded as transitory or per-manent—or, to put the thing fairly—non-transitory? Gentle-men, you now perhaps begin to apprehend the kind of diffi-culties which confront me in this case. But I do not know why I am troubling you with all this: for these are things that I have to decide alone. The truth is, I am thinking aloud. And, I tell you what, I am going to make you help me as much as I can. After all, this may be the last case I try. Get your pencils, gentlemen: and do try, his Lordship added testily, to keep awake. We shan't get lunch for another hour and a half.

The Judge left the following questions to the jury:

(*a*) Were any of the signals complained of defamatory?

(*b*) Which?

(*c*) Why?

(*d*) Were there, in fact, any dead rats in M/Y *Perfume II*?

(*e*) If so, does it matter?

(*f*) Do you believe a single word that Mr. Haddock says?

(*g*) If 'yes,' give examples.

(*h*) Between ourselves, don't you think the plaintiff is a fairly unsympathetic character?

(*i*) Have you the faintest idea, after all my laborious discourse:
    (i) What is the difference between libel and slander?
    (ii) Why?

(*j*) If 'yes,' would you say that flag-signals were:
    (i) Transitory?
    (ii) Non-transitory?

(*k*) And, if you were in my place, though, mind you, this is my job, not yours, would you say that this was a case of libel or slander?

(*l*) (i) Why?
    (ii) Why not?

(*m*) What damages:
    (i) Against Mr. Hume?
    (ii) Against Mr. Haddock?

(*n*) You may have to find for the plaintiff: but, honestly, if you were me, would you give him any costs?

(*o*) By the way, I forgot to ask you—do you think that the plaintiff's reputation has suffered?

(*p*) If 'yes,' does this upset you?

(*q*) Now will you retire, please? And come back soon.

The jury retired, for seventeen hours. On their return, the Foreman said: My Lord, we are a little confused. We disagree on almost every particular.

His Lordship: Well done. I think you are quite right.

Sir Eliot Ember, for the plaintiff, asked for costs.

The Judge: Well, no. You see, I have decided to strike Mr. Haddock out of the action as he was not the master of the ship. And Mr. Hume has behaved very decently throughout. So I am afraid the plaintiff will have to pay all the costs.

Sir Eliot: If your Lordship pleases.

Sir Ronald Rutt: Shall we have a new trial?

The Judge: Not before me. Why don't you appeal? Your father would love this case.[1]

3 October, 1951

NOTE: Lovers of the law of libel, that unique English heritage, must regret that yet one more problem has, after all, failed to find a solution, as it were, at the post. The celebrated case of *Chicken* v. *Ham* [2 H.L. 1926] will be in the minds of many students. There the question was whether defamatory words spoken deliberately through a gramophone record were in the nature of libel or slander. There

[1] Sir Ethelred Rutt, K.C., was recently appointed a Lord Justice of Appeal.

were two trials of the action, and two appeals to the Court of Appeal, which arrived, unhappily, at two contradictory conclusions. Finally, in the House of Lords, two Lords of Appeal were for 'libel,' and two were for 'slander': Lord Goat was about to deliver what would have been the fifth, and (presumably) decisive, opinion when, most unfortunately, he perished of a heart-attack. So the point remains *in dubio*. Now we have the signal-flags. Lord Lick in the gramophone case (above) mentioned *Silvertop* v. *the Stepney Guardians* where (he said) a man trained a parrot to say three times after meals, '*Councillor Wart has not washed to-day.*' 'It was held,' his Lordship asserted, 'that this was a libel.' With the greatest respect to a most distinguished judge and public servant, it must now be said that prolonged researches have failed to disclose any authentic report of *Silvertop* v. *the Stepney Guardians*. This is a pity. For a parrot trained to utter the same insult at regular intervals would seem, *prima facie*, to provide such an element of continuity as might serve to convert the spoken slander into libel: and from the intermittent, recurring parrot-cry to the intermittent, recurring signal-flag might have been an easy step.

Some passage across a border-line too strictly drawn is evidently desirable. There is now the 'loud-hailer,' an instrument by which the spoken word can be carried over very wide spaces and, in urban districts, to the ears of many thousands. A hearer, however much he may resent what is said through this machine, is quite incapable of replying to the speaker—or, at the same range of sound, to anyone else; and, what is more, though the utterance may damage him in the minds of millions, he is still restricted to the remedies for 'word-of-mouth' slander. The case of *Taylor* v. *Twerp* is worthy of note, although—or indeed, because—it never came into court. Taylor was the 'official' Conservative candidate for Burbleton at a General Election. He had been the Member for Burbleton, and lived in Burbleton, for many years. Twerp, a London journalist, who was a candidate too, went round the town in a van with a loud-hailer through which he, or his assistants, cried, hour after hour, and day after day: 'GEORGE TAYLOR IS A LIAR—L-I-A-R—LIAR!' There was nothing at all behind this accusation: and Taylor was willing to ignore it. But his friends persuaded him that, in his own 'home-town,' he would be expected to take notice of an assault upon his honour so powerful and so persistent. He issued a writ. Considerable costs were incurred in the preparation of the case. But at the election Taylor was triumphantly returned and Twerp lost his deposit.

Taylor's lawyer then had to explain to him (a) that the insults, since they were spoken, not written, were slander, not libel; (b) that therefore he would have to prove 'actual damage'; and (c) that, since he had been elected, he could do no such thing. The writ was withdrawn, which, the ignorant said, showed that there was something in the accusations.

In my Law of Libel Bill of July, 1938—and also in my second Bill, introduced by Sir Stanley Reed on 3 February, 1939—I proposed to assimilate the law of slander to the law of libel. In evidence before the very distinguished Porter Committee I urged the same course, and I told the learned gentlemen the story of *Taylor* v. *Twerp*. With two dissentients, they rejected my proposal. They did say, 'We consider that all defamatory broadcast statements should be treated as libels': but they meant only 'statements or images broadcast by radiotransmission,' so they would not help poor Mr. Taylor at all. Mr. Richard O'Sullivan, K.C., and Professor E. C. S. Wade (bless them!) were on my side: 'They consider that no adequate reason now exists for perpetuating a distinction which originated by an accident of English legal history, finds no place in Scots law, and has led to a confusing volume of case-law.'

Concerning the 'accident of legal history,' see a speech by one of the burgesses for Oxford University (*Hansard*, February 3, 1939, Col. 585):

'It often happens that such distinctions arise from historical causes, and because we are too lazy to remove them or amend them we create an elaborate philosophical defence of them which we pretend has been there all the time. . . . Slander was dealt with in the beginning by the feudal courts, and then by ecclesiastical courts. Then printing came in and the Star Chamber leapt upon printing, and an action for libel has retained some of the criminal character of that court's proceedings and no proof of damage is required. Now we say that because a written wrong is a solid, enduring, fundamental thing therefore it must be made more easy for the victim to pursue it. I should submit that the contrary was the case; the whispered slander is far more difficult to catch, and therefore the distinction, if any, should perhaps be the other way round. At all events, it is surely absurd to say that what is written on a postcard is more dangerous than what is shouted at a mass meeting, perhaps through a loudspeaker. However, that is the law as it stands to-day.'

To-day, likewise.

On 1 February, 1952, Mr. Harold Lever (Labour), a 'private' Member, introduced a Bill founded on the excellent Porter Committee's Report. It obtained a Second Reading, and, when these reports left the editor's hands, looked like becoming law. The Porter Committee was the direct result of the editor's 1938 Bills, and he applauds their labours and Mr. Lever's efforts with a grandfatherly interest and pride.

(24) REX *v.* RUNGLE

AT the Old Bailey to-day, after counsel's closing speeches in the Burbleton Burglar case, the aged Mr. Justice Codd summed up to the jury. He said:

Gentlemen of the jury, this is a trial for murder—or maybe manslaughter. A man's life hangs—pardon—depends upon your decision: and you will, I know, approach your task with due solemnity. So do I. But this is the last case that I shall ever try. Once I'm back in the old flannel bags in the garden that old Chief will never coax me into a court again, whatever epidemics may decimate the Bench. You, gentlemen, have spent two or three days in a court of law, and already you are longing to get back to civilization. I have been here for fifty years. Imagine it! Fifty years of quarrelling and crime, quibbles and costs, adulteries, assaults, burglaries and motor-accidents. 'Running-down cases' we call them. Remember the story about old Hewart, when he was Lord Chief Justice? Someone asked him how he enjoyed his life on the Bench. 'It's all right,' he said, 'when any legal business crops up. But I seem to spend most of my time adjudicating on disputes between insurance companies arising out of collisions between two stationary motor-cars, each on the right side of the road, and blowing its horn.' Ha! Yes, I thought you'd like that. Don't look so shocked, Sir Roger. Mind you, gentlemen, I'm not complaining. We like the life, of course: and we live a long time, I can't think why. But fifty years, you may decide, is just about enough. You may think, having heard all the evidence—pardon me, I was forgetting—you want to hear about this case.

Well, there is the prisoner, George Rungle. He's killed a burglar, there's no doubt about that. But he looks a good chap, you must agree. I believe he is a good chap: and I may as well tell you at once that I'm on his side——

Sir Roger Wheedle (for the Crown): Milord! The jury can hardly——

The Judge: Of course, Sir Roger doesn't like that. I didn't expect he would. By the way, gentlemen, that's another big thing about my future. I shan't have to listen to any more speeches by my dear old colleague, Sir Roger Wheedle. You've heard one or two. I don't say they're not *good* speeches—they are: but you know what I mean. Going up now, aren't you, Sir Roger? Treasury briefs and all! The next thing, you'll be Solicitor-General. Which are you going to be, Conservative or Labour? Difficult to say just now, I suppose. Anyhow, you'll go far. You'll never sink to the Bench, like me. £5,000 a year, less 2. Well, about this case. As I have said, there's no doubt that Mr. Rungle killed this burglar.

Sir Ronald Rutt (for the defence): Milord, with great respect, that *is* one of the points on which——

The Judge: Now, what's the matter with you, Sir Ronald? By the way, how's your father? Dear old Ethelred! The battles we used to have! And how your dear father used to bristle! 'Bristle'! Yes, that's the word. And now he's up in the Court of Appeal. 'Lord Justice Rutt.' Soon be a Lord of Appeal, I shouldn't wonder. 'Baron Rutt.' I shall laugh, rather. Old Wool's there already. Can't be a day less than 103. But there he is; blowing off like a juvenile grampus. You've done well, too, young Ronald. I can see you President of the Board of Trade. And I'm still a miserable *puisne* in the King's Bench Division. To-morrow I'll be plain Sir Humphrey Codd again. Never mind. About this case:

The prisoner killed the burglar. And what a good thing! If I have a chance, I'll kill a burglar too. What's more, it ought to be a capital offence. I never know why they make so much fuss about blackmail. After all, there couldn't be any blackmail if there wasn't something black to go upon. But these little squits of burglars—they creep into strange houses, poor houses too, frighten innocent old women and steal their

K

wedding-rings. That's what this beast-boy had been doing for months! House after house. The police have got any number of——

Sir Roger Wheedle: With the greatest respect, milord——

The Judge: I know exactly what you're going to say, Sir Roger. So don't bother. That's what I think about burglars. You may say what you like about 'our barbarous ancestors,' but in this department they knew a thing or two. In the eighteenth century—time of the *Beggar's Opera*—they were pretty harsh about stealing. They had to be. No police—no street-lamps—nothing. But they distinguished. If you stole property valued at five shillings you were hanged. If you stole from the person to the value of 1s., or from a dwelling-house to the value of 40s., you were hanged. But the juries were merciful, and scaled things down, if they liked your face. One Catherine Delavan, I remember, stole nine guineas and 11s.: but the jury found her guilty to the value of 4s. 10d. only. You see the point, Sir Roger? She was transported, not hanged.

Sir Roger Wheedle: The point is taken, milord.

The Judge: But there were two cases where no jury could save your neck. If you put people 'in Fear on the Highway,' or if you burgled—that is, broke into a house *by night*—values didn't matter, and you were hanged, however little you stole. The same principle, no doubt—'putting people in *fear*'—whether it was the highway or the house. When the deceased beast-boy had been at it for a month or two not a woman in the neighbourhood could sleep peacefully in her bed. At the smallest sound, the creak of a stair, the bang of a shutter, everyone in the house sat up sweating with alarm. That's why they hanged them in the eighteenth century, and that's why we ought to hang them now. The prisoner, of course, popped ahead and killed the burglar himself: and I must say that I'm delighted.

Sir Ronald Rutt: Milord——

Sir Roger Wheedle: Milord, with great respect, the laws of the eighteenth century are hardly on all fours with——

The Judge: All right, Sir Roger, let's come to the nineteenth century. Are you familiar with *Purcell's Case?*

Sir Roger Wheedle: No, milord.

The Judge: Well, Mr. Purcell was a septuagenarian, of County Cork. And in 1811 he was knighted—*knighted*, Sir Roger—for killing four burglars with a carving-knife. Pretty good, eh?

Sir Roger Wheedle: That, no doubt, was in self-defence, milord. In the present case, the deceased was offering no violence and in fact was leaving the premises.

The Judge: But he had offered violence, he had committed a violent felony, and he was escaping. You see what it is, members of the jury? They're trying to whittle down our ancient rights. It's all part of this namby-pamby stuff about crime. I expect Sir Roger Wheedle's heart is bleeding for the deceased, the little pest. What was the burglar's name, Sir Roger?

Sir Roger: Moss, milord. And may I add, milord, that I am only trying to seek the truth and to do my duty according to law.

The Judge: Of course, Sir Roger, of course! Don't excite yourself. But you know Moss's record as well as I do. Left a good home and joined a gang. Began coshing at the age of twelve. Brought up in luxury at remand schools and approved schools and Lord knows what. Had every chance. Never done a day's work. Doesn't mind prison because it's all so cosy now. Keeps a whole neighbourhood in terror for weeks. And when he catches it at last we're told an unkind charwoman shut him in a cupboard when he was a child, and he's never been the same since. He's a pathological case or a psychological misfit.[1] Ha! Stuff and nonsense! Suffers from 'frustration.' Frustration, indeed! I wonder how they'd like to be a judge in these days, drawing the same pay for the last 100 years and more!

[1] See *Rex* v. *Lout* (1951), where a youth was charged with robbery with violence and other offences. His father said: 'At the age of fourteen he fell out of a tree. Since then he's been a different boy.'

Sir Roger: Milord, with great respect, the character of the deceased is not strictly——

The Judge: I know. I know. I'm wandering, Sir Roger. But you provoked me. What I mean is that no one seems to bother about the psychology of the poor old men and women who lie shivering in their beds when a beast-boy's about. And when he gets his deserts——

Sir Roger: Milord!

The Judge: Don't interrupt, Sir Roger. We must get on. Now, jurymen all, recall what happened. Mr. Rungle, having no firearms, kept an ordinary garden-fork by his bed, as we all ought to do. That, or a hat-pin. At two o'clock in the morning he hears noises below; he takes his garden-fork, slips downstairs, and finds Moss, in a mask, filling a bag with the Rungle goods and belongings. Moss held a pistol at him (it wasn't loaded, but Rungle was not to know that), and in the childish language of his kind, said: 'Stick 'em up. This is a stick-up.' Rungle bravely, and rather wittily, replied, raising his garden-fork: 'Oh, is it? And this is a stick-*in*!' Ha!

When the bold burglar saw the garden-fork, he uttered a yell of terror, turned and made for the window. Mr. Rungle cried, 'Stop!' meaning to arrest him; but Moss did not stop. As he was passing through the window the prisoner threw the garden-fork after him, harpoon-fashion: it pierced the burglar's heart and he died.

Now, the Crown, rather mildly, it is true, suggest to you that this was Murder. The defence say that it was Justifiable Homicide.

Sir Roger, I know, does not think that I know any law: though in fifty years one does pick up some scraps of information. So I have been looking up the authorities, and, in these soft days, it does appear that there is some doubt. In one tremendous tome (under *Burglary*) I read:

The question whether and how far it is justifiable to kill a burglar is by no means clear. If violence on the part of the burglar is reasonably apprehended, it is not murder to shoot him dead with intent to kill him, but whether it is justifiable to kill merely in defence of property is doubtful.

But in another page of the same tome I find two of the categories of Justifiable Homicide set out as follows:

(*d*) Where an officer or his assistant, in the due execution of his office, arrests or attempts to arrest a person for *felony*, or a dangerous wound given, and he having notice thereof flies and is killed by such officer or assistant in pursuit.

(*e*) Where upon such offence as last described *a private person* in whose sight it has been committed arrests or endeavours to arrest the offender, and kills him in resistance or flight, in similar circumstances.

Note, gentlemen, that burglary is a felony, and a violent felony.

I turned then to Mr. Kenny's admirable *Outlines of Criminal Law*.[1] Here again I wandered, as one wanders in a wood, now in sunlight, now in the shade. First I was told, with some discouragement, that:

When the wrongdoer is not going so far as to assault a human being, but is only *interfering unlawfully with property*, whether real or personal, the possessor of that property (though he is permitted by the law to use a moderate degree of force in defence of his possessions) will usually not be justified in carrying this force to the point of killing the trespasser. . . .

But then I passed into the light:

Such a justification will not arise unless the trespasser's interference or resistance amounts to a felony, and moreover to a felony of some kind that is violent, such for example, as robbery, arson or *burglary*.

One more step and I was in the shade again:

Even these extremely violent felonies should not be resisted by extreme violence unless it is actually necessary; thus, fire-arms should not be used unless there seems to be no other mode ('Mode!' I like 'mode', don't you?) available for defeating the intruder *and securing his arrest*.

[1] Cambridge University Press.

Sir Roger Wheedle: Your Lordship, no doubt, remembers the case of *Rex* v. *Cooper?*

The Judge: You mean that case in 1641? At the Surrey Assizes?

Sir Roger: Yes, milord.

The Judge: Of course. But I don't see that it helps you much. That was another window case. Cooper struck a burglar in the eye with a spit. And was acquitted.

Sir Roger: Yes, milord. But, milord, I should be prepared to distinguish.

The Judge: You can't distinguish any more. Well, gentlemen, there you are. The Crown's case, I gather—and, by the way, I'm not sure that they believe in it very strongly, but they think, in these days, they have to be as soft as they can— where was I? Oh, yes, the Crown's case is that Rungle was not being attacked, and was in no danger himself; that the deceased beast-boy was merely interfering, or had merely interfered, with property (and property, of course, is very unpopular nowadays), therefore the prisoner was entitled only to use *reasonable* force: to stick a man through the heart with a garden-fork was more than reasonable in the circumstances, and therefore the killing was murder. Is that a fair statement of your case, Sir Roger?

Sir Roger: Yes, milord. I might add, of course——

The Judge: But you mayn't. Now, gentlemen of the jury, I must not, of course, attempt to influence you unduly (what an idea!). But let me tell you the story as I see it in the light of the law, as I understand it.

The deceased Moss committed a burglary. At Common Law this crime is committed when a dwelling-house or a church is broken and entered at night with the intention of committing some felony therein. Section 51 of the Larceny Act, 1861, extended the definition:

Whosoever shall enter the dwelling-house of another with intent to commit any felony therein, or being in the said dwelling-house shall commit any felony therein, and shall in either case break out of the said dwelling-house in the night, shall be deemed guilty of burglary.

Now, burglary, I say again, is a felony and a 'violent' felony. It is a continuing offence. A man is a burglar from the time he breaks in till the time he breaks out. He does not cease to be a burglar if, having robbed the house, he sits down in an armchair and peaceably recites the poems of Keats. In this case he made a feeble threat of violence to the householder: but I am willing to forget that, if it pleases Sir Roger; for it is not necessary to my argument. The big point is that the house-holder finds the felon at work; that not only his instinct, and his interest, but his public duty instruct and oblige him to arrest the felon, if he can, and to hand him over to justice. There have been numerous burglaries in the neighbourhood which have gone unpunished (few indeed are the arrested burglars anywhere, and sadly few the stolen goods recovered). A householder is in the position of an unofficial police officer: if he lets the felon go he will be letting loose a menace to who knows how many other defenceless homes. Accordingly he orders the felon to 'Stop!' But the felon ('he having notice thereof') makes off. What is the householder to do? He can only use the nearest weapon to his hand. If Mr. Rungle had had a fire-arm he would have been well entitled to shoot the burglar in the leg, at least. As it was, he had only a garden-fork. He did not, I am sure, intend to kill the burglar. The one thought, the proper thought, in his mind, was 'I must stop him' (and let us not forget that the word 'arrest' means 'stop'). It is regrettable perhaps (though not, I think, very much) that his only weapon had the result it did: but for that there is nobody to blame but the burglar. As the harsh but wholesome saying goes, 'He should have thought of that before'—before, that is, he entered upon a crime which has rightly earned especial detestation from the State.

Now, gentlemen, I have done. I should not like my last judicial utterance to be quoted as something exceptional, relevant only to the circumstances of a special case. No, Sir

Roger, since there appears to be some doubt in this important corner of life and law, I declare the law to be as follows:

'It is the right and duty of any householder, or any other honest citizen, who finds an undoubted burglar in a dwelling-house, to arrest him. He may, and should, order the burglar to stay quietly on the premises till any necessary arrangements have been made. If the burglar disobeys this order and attempts to make off, the honest citizen may use any force he considers necessary and any weapon that is at hand to stop him: and if the result is death it is justifiable homicide; not murder, or even manslaughter.'

But, of course, gentlemen, you are the jury: and you are well entitled to say that I am talking nonsense. Pray consider your verdict.

The Foreman stood up and called for three cheers for his Lordship. Then, without leaving the box, they found the prisoner Not Guilty.

The Judge: Discharge the prisoner. Goodbye, Mr. Rungle. Kill all the burglars you can. But don't forget to say 'Stop!'

Sir Roger Wheedle: Milord, if you can stand one more speech from me, I should like, on behalf of the Bar, to wish you a long and happy retirement.

Sir Ronald Rutt: I too, milord.

The Judge: Well that's very handsome of you both. I must say I've enjoyed my last case considerably. If you aren't careful, I shall come back after all.

7 September, 1951

NOTE: Since this case, the police inform us, the burglary rate has shown a marked decline.

INDEX

Printed in Great Britain by
The Camelot Press Ltd., London and Southampton